I'VE

GOT

MY JOURNEY TO MOTHERHOOD

THIS

COLETTE CENTENO FOX

I'VE

GOT

MY JOURNEY TO MOTHERHOOD

THIS

The Book Guild Ltd

First published in Great Britain in 2020 by
The Book Guild Ltd
9 Priory Business Park
Wistow Road, Kibworth
Leicestershire, LE8 0RX
Freephone: 0800 999 2982
www.bookguild.co.uk
Email: info@bookguild.co.uk
Twitter: @bookguild

Typeset in 11pt Minion Pro

Printed and bound by CPI Group (UK) Ltd, Croydon, CR0 4YY

ISBN 978 1913208 486

British Library Cataloguing in Publication Data.

A catalogue record for this book is available from the British Library.

For my husband, Michael,
and my children, Ethan and Gabrielle.

CONTENTS

ACKNOWLEDGEMENTS

I really want to thank my husband... He was the one who had to put up with me. That he did so with love and patience and encouragement instead of strangling me, meant the world.

My family and relatives: thank you for fighting my battles in my absence. I love you all.

Dr. Atalla and Dr. Shehata, thank you for never giving up on me, and for the endless encouragement, I'm forever grateful.

My friends: Lala, Emma, Rhiana, Grace, and Stefanie, I am so grateful to have found such loyal friends I can constantly rely on. Even though we don't see each other often, I know you are always there for me no matter what.

one

MASKED HAPPINESS

WAKING UP, I SMILED at my husband. I was filled with a mix of emotions: happiness, relief, and a concealed sadness. My husband, Mike, was sitting with our babies nestled in his arms; I was lucky. Don't get me wrong; I was over the moon, yet at the same time, I contemplated retrospectively.

This should have happened years ago. The sadness I felt while watching my husband and children reminded me of what should have been. I've learned that sometimes the things people find easiest in life can in fact be someone else's biggest battle.

My story began back in the summer of 2006. I was waiting to sit my final exam at university. I was in my final year studying for a BSc degree in Travel and Hospitality Management. I had put off relationships, as I saw them as a hindrance. I was easily distracted. If I dated, I knew that I would have missed a lot of lectures. A relationship was something I did not need and wasn't looking for.

I still had fun though; I still socialised, partied, and travelled abroad with friends like any other young woman. I just avoided dating.

Around the time that I finished my final examination, I was working in a local lounge bar in East London called Sway. On one of my night shifts, Grayson approached me. He was tall at six foot two, slim and muscular, with thick, short, auburn red hair. His rugged features were alluring and captivating. He was courteous, charming, and generous. Grayson was a builder by profession. I was instantly attracted to him. We exchanged numbers and eventually dated.

I discovered that he had a son, Brandon, from a previous relationship, who was four, with long, blond hair and a gentle, playful manner. Brandon's mum, Louisa, and I got along, which was favourable because it meant she trusted me with her precious son when we looked after him every other weekend.

Our relationship was blooming. I was glad I had waited to date as, if not, I may have missed out on meeting him.

Several months passed, and Grayson purchased a house that needed to be renovated and desperately needed modernisation. During the evenings and at weekends, he would be busy gutting out and redesigning the house so that we could move into it together. It would be a family home for Grayson, Brandon and I.

Only two dark clouds were hanging over our relationship. Firstly, Grayson suffered from unpredictable changes in mood. In particular, he had sudden bouts of gloominess and sullenness. Also, he wasn't very smart with his money and would often be left short due to bouts of frivolousness.

We had discussed having kids together but decided it would be for the distant future. I was happy; we were happy. Grayson seemed perfectly content with it being just the three of us.

Two years later, in August 2008, I was working for a local company, specialising in USA travel. Grayson and I were still together, and although he had been working a lot on the house, it was nonetheless incomplete. Furthermore, at this point we were not living together. I was residing in my flat just on the outskirts of London, approximately ten minutes from the house he had purchased. I was twenty-seven at the time, and even though we were enjoying our relationship, as a couple neither of us felt ready for the lifelong commitment of children.

One day I sat at home waiting for my friend Stef to come over. We were planning on going out for a jog. She was a good friend whom I'd met while working at Sway. We worked a lot of our shifts together and became close. When we weren't out socialising, we would hang out or sit on my couch chatting, venting, laughing, and putting the world to rights. We had been friends for approximately five years.

Stef was always quite the beauty; she was of fair complexion with mid-length wisps of golden blonde hair with the right hint of a wave. Her hair always seemed to capture the light just right. She also had the kindest pair of soft, brown eyes, which always held a tiny warmth within them; she was free-spirited and gentle. I was lucky to have such a loyal and trustworthy friend.

Whilst we were out jogging, I stopped and said to her, "I'm feeling really queasy,"

She asked me, "Are you pregnant?".

I was taken aback by her comment, as the thought had never crossed my mind. "I don't know," I answered, honestly.

The following day, I was sitting in my flat, contemplating what could be wrong. Was Stef right? I didn't feel right; I had felt off for a few days. As I sat there, I realised I had actually missed my period, and so I rushed out to buy pregnancy tests – yes, plural; I needed to be sure.

Sitting in the bathroom, I took a test, then, upon seeing the positive result, I took another. I continued taking loads of tests. I wanted to be sure I was reading them correctly. After taking several tests, it was evident – I was pregnant. I didn't know how to feel about it.

I wasn't prepared for such a major life change; we hadn't decided to have a baby; in fact, we had actively postponed this until well into the future. I had no idea how to feel about the whole concept. I loved children, always had, I just was not sure if it was the right time for us.

Stef was the first person that I told about the news of the pregnancy. She was delighted for me. Stef knew my situation and she was so supportive. She always had time to listen to how I was feeling. I explained how I (we) didn't think now was the right time, but that I felt like I wanted to keep the baby.

When I told Grayson, he was genuinely happy about the pregnancy, and we started planning. It helped, knowing he was on board with it all and that he was just as happy as I was.

September arrived, and I found myself even more thrilled about the idea. I had a two-seater car at the time, which I decided to sell. After all, I needed to buy something a little more family-friendly. We were making all kinds of plans, making sure we were prepared for the baby's arrival. I became more enthusiastic each week. I was following the online guides to see how big the baby was growing. I imagined life with a baby; I would hold my hand across my stomach, waiting for the day when I would feel my baby move.

I was still naive, though. I had not considered or witnessed what could go wrong during a pregnancy. I had my head in the sand, deep in the sand.

I had booked an appointment with my GP at four weeks to find out what the next step was, as I had no experience or concept of what to do.

At eight weeks, I was referred to the health clinic. There, I went to the appointment alone. I sat, waiting to be called through. A young woman came out and called my name. She was in her late twenties and seemed newly qualified, but I still felt like I was in good hands.

In the office, she took me through some routine questions and a small examination. Then, towards the end of the appointment, she asked if I would like to hear the baby's heartbeat on the Doppler. I was enthusiastic and agreed. I lay on the bed, with my top pulled up, showing my small, almost-unnoticeable bump. The midwife rubbed the gel onto my stomach and pushed the Doppler down, moving it around trying to find the heartbeat.

After a while, she explained, "I am unable to detect the heartbeat. There is nothing to worry about, though. There could be several reasons for not finding the heartbeat, such as the position the baby is lying in or the stage of your pregnancy."

"Okay, thank you," I said, accepting the midwife's assurances this was all normal. I was given a date for my first scan, the twelve-week scan, which would be in four weeks, at which point the heartbeat would be more apparent. With that in mind, I didn't anticipate any problems.

The next four weeks passed quickly. I grew even more elated, which caught me by surprise. The shock of being pregnant had now mellowed. We were more relaxed about the direction in the way things were moving. Everything was falling into place.

My appointment at the antenatal clinic was on October 15th, and I had just learnt our baby was as big as a lime. This knowledge helped me envision the baby and its size and features. I had grown to love the baby I had not met and was slowly adapting my life for the change that would soon come.

I attended the appointment with my friend, Stef. It was just the two of us as a contractor employed Grayson at the time. Even though he tried to make it, he couldn't get the time off work. I would have loved him to be there, but I had to get used to it. Grayson worked a lot, and sometimes, he wouldn't be able to attend appointments.

We sat down in the waiting room, and as my name was called, I stood up and said, "Stef, could you wait in the waiting area? I want to be alone when I see the first glimpse of my baby."

"Of course," Stef said with a smile.

I followed the sonographer into one of the consultation rooms for my routine dating scan. The lady was around five foot four in her late forties, with dark, shoulder-length hair. She was a friendly Irish woman. Her welcoming nature helped me to calm my nerves. The room was painted cream. There was nothing in the way of decoration, just a limp curtain closing off the bed and computer monitor. The sonographer asked me a few questions, and then the lights were dimmed. I was asked to lay down on the bed. I waited eagerly for her to begin.

She asked me, "Lower your skirt to your hips and raise your top to your chest."

I did so. She then tucked tissue around my clothing to protect it from the gel. Once she spread the cold gel across my lower abdomen, she passed the scanner over the gel and pressed down until my uterus could be seen on the monitor. I observed as she gently tried finding the baby. Her face was indifferent, as though this was an everyday thing, which for her, I suppose, it was. I couldn't see the screen as she had it turned away from me. I assumed she was just doing the usual checks before telling me anything.

Then I saw the change in her expression – a sorrowful look etched on her face, which she quickly tried to hide from me.

Saddened, she turned and explained, "I can't detect the baby's heartbeat."

I didn't know what she meant at that moment. I waited for her to reassure me it was normal, just like the midwife had.

She went on to explain, "The baby you are carrying stopped growing at eleven weeks. It is a non-viable pregnancy."

I felt devastated. I had grown to love my baby, and I realised just how much I wanted it. It is true what they say: a mother loves her baby from the moment she finds out she is pregnant, even if the pregnancy comes at a difficult or unexpected time.

"Please give me a moment," I said, stumbling out of the room.

Walking out the door, I saw Stef waiting for me; she stood there smiling at me, anticipating the good news that would never come. I tried so hard to suppress my emotions.

"I've lost the baby."

As the words left my mouth, the feeling I had overwhelmed me, and I burst into tears, my body trembling. I could not think of anything other than grief. I couldn't even remember if there were other people in the waiting room looking at me. Were people staring at me? Did they know the news I had just been given? Stef opened her arms and embraced me. I was speechless, but she didn't need the words to understand what had happened.

I vaguely remembered walking through a cylindrical walkway with her to another part of the hospital. The walk felt like it would never end, but we finally reached a tiny waiting area. There was a tiny, black, wooden coffee table holding leaflets with information about counselling and grieving, along with a selection of health magazines. Underneath it was a dull, grey carpet, which covered the whole room. A television hung in one corner displaying boring TV adverts. We just sat silently for a while.

Once I had processed the bad news, and I had come to terms with carrying a dead baby, I decided I needed to let others know.

So, with shaking hands, I called my mum first. She was travelling around Asia at the time. I was dreading this phone call, as it was her much-awaited first grandchild. At first, I was anxious to bring up the topic. I was overcome with sadness as I told her.

"Are you sure?" she asked. "What happened?" All the questions I could not answer. I explained what I had been told by the nurses, so she would understand what happened. She said, "Call your dad and let him know, as well."

I dialled my dad after. My dad knew nothing about the situation I was in, so I had to explain it all: that I was pregnant, but that I had lost the baby, in the same phone call.

This was difficult. I had pictured the moment I would tell him, never dreaming I would have to give bad news at the same time. My dad wasn't a man of many words, so the conversation was brief. Maybe he didn't know what to say, or maybe it was just all too unfamiliar. He expressed a few words of kindness, yet the tone of his voice seemed unimpressed. I knew he wasn't a fan of Grayson, but he did not say anything unpleasant.

All I could do was cry; I felt desolate, the tears rolling down my cheeks as I tried to comprehend what had occured. My mind was stuck, fighting to find out how this happened. Stef stayed by my side as I curled up into a ball; she cradled and comforted me. She kept me afloat in the deep water I was drowning in.

We returned to the doctor's office. As my name was called, I stood up anxiously; I turned to Stef.

"Did you want me to come in with you?" she asked.

After contemplating, I said, "I'd prefer to go alone. But don't worry, I'm fine."

She nodded, smiled at me and sat back down in the dull, lifeless waiting area until I was finished.

While waiting for the doctor to enter, alone, I stared at the empty, white wall in front of me; I felt a build-up of tension and anxiety. My mind was a tangled web of emotions, but the biggest two were emptiness and heartache. The doctor gave me a compassionate smile.

"I'm sorry for your loss," were his first words uttered to me. I held back my tears as he said that I had experienced a silent miscarriage. "Regrettably, you wouldn't have realised that anything had gone wrong. There aren't any warning signs, such as bleeding or pain. Your body keeps developing, but the sac is either empty, or the embryo had stopped growing. Instead of waiting for you to miscarry naturally, we will use a treatment called medical management. You will be given medication to help speed up the process of a miscarriage."

When someone explains that your baby is no longer

alive, it is like you become two people. One half of you wants the baby out, and the other just never wants to let go because that means losing the baby forever. It was like a battle; you knew which option you should choose yet you still struggle to accept it.

Stef stayed at the hospital with me during the day. I called Grayson. I had to tell him straight away; as it wouldn't be right to text him or wait until we next saw each other. During the phone call, he didn't have much of a reaction – a little taken aback. I think he also found the situation hard to comprehend.

All that the hospital could do at that moment was to discharge me. They gave me a date for a follow-up appointment at Whipps Cross; this was to see a different consultant. Just like that, I was sent home. I had no idea that this heartbreak would be just one of many to come and the beginning of a long, agonising journey.

As the week passed, Stef was regularly checking up on me to make sure I was okay. I was lucky to have her.

Meanwhile, Grayson was busy working and renovating the property. He had made good progress, and the house was now in a liveable condition. He had been rushing to finish so that it would be ready in time for our baby's arrival. Instead, the date arrived for me to go to Whipps Cross Hospital. My appointment was at 7am. I knew I couldn't be late. I was warned that I would need to stay for up to six hours after the tablet was given or until after I had passed the pregnancy.

Upon entering Whipps Cross, I reported to the desk of the ward. The nurse signed me in and asked me to follow her.

My sister, Chantal, and Grayson had accompanied me to the hospital; they both wanted to help support me through what was to come.

"Well, here we are." The nurse smiled kindly as she opened the door to a private room. An IV drip and oxygen tanks surrounded the bed. An old TV hung from the ceiling, and the window opened onto the (not so lovely) busy car park. In the corner were two chairs, frayed with wear and tear. It was a typical hospital room – sparse and functional. I had my own private bathroom, which I was grateful for. The nurse then handed me a pair of green knee-high deep vein thrombosis socks and an off-white tattered hospital gown to dress myself in. It felt strange; this was the second time I had been admitted to a hospital. The first time was for the extraction of my wisdom teeth.

I changed into the gown and put on the socks, and then I sat and waited, wondering what would happen next.

The doctor came in and explained, "Since your miscarriage will not be a natural one, there is a risk of infection. So, we need to get started straightaway in inducing labour."

I was given Misoprostol – a pill given to help my body miscarry sooner. It worked by preparing my cervix and making my womb contract to help push out the pregnancy. At that moment, I had no concept of just how painful the whole experience would be.

The nurse came in and sat next to me as she explained the process, "The Misoprostol will cause you to bleed, and you will experience pain and cramps within one to four hours of taking the tablet." The nurse also gave me medication to help with nausea, and a paper bedpan to empty the pregnancy remains into.

Sitting, just waiting for the tablet to kick in, Chantal and Grayson, were eating McDonald's and chitchatting like it was any normal day. I was upset and hurting, yet they carried on as though nothing had happened. I couldn't blame them, though. They had nothing to do, everything was down to my body, and it was a case of sitting and waiting.

It had been an hour when the cramps started. They began mildly and irregularly. I felt a slight discomfort at first, which I dismissed as nothing. I was messing about, not realising it was the onset. The pain intensified, and I started to get cold sweats. Pretty soon, I was clenching my clammy fists with every contraction.

The nurse would return frequently to check on me, more to see if anything had passed than to take any action. She would ask, "How are you feeling? Do you need anything?" It was just another sign; there was not much anyone could do to help this time pass quicker.

Within a couple of hours, I was bent over double, holding onto the side of the bed, trying to find a comfortable position. I felt like I was an outsider looking in at myself. Grayson and Chantal were still sitting, chatting away as I struggled to control the waves of the contractions. They offered me a chocolate milkshake, and as much as I would never normally turn down a milkshake, I couldn't move. I wanted it all to be over with.

I kept continuously calling the nurse. "Can you give me something to help relieve the pain?"

"We can give you either painkillers or gas and air, which would you like?"

"The painkillers please."

However, I didn't realise it would take a few hours of chasing before I would receive them. For some reason, the nurse refrained from giving me any pain relief. She would return regularly empty-handed, despite my constant reminders and begging.

I was allowed to eat and drink, but I couldn't bring myself to. The dull aches in my back and lower abdomen, along with the pressure in my pelvis, were too severe, plus I had lost my appetite. I circled the room, trying to ease the contractions.

I became bored with my room, so, I wandered around the long, narrow hallway. Without hesitation, I pushed open the heavy double doors with my body weight, and the draft hit my face: warm and with a tincture of bleach. Ahead of me, there were painted walls decorated with black-and-white photographs of hospital staff, most now likely deceased or in their nineties.

After a few minutes, I heard my sister calling, "The doctor is here."

I waddled back to my dull, lifeless room. I felt relief; I wasn't sure why, but knowing the doctor was there to see me helped.

The doctor explained, "I came to check on your progress and condition."

He analysed my chart and performed a pelvic exam to check whether my cervix was dilated. He felt my lower abdomen. Just like when the nurse came in, it was mostly questions and a check-up. No one could do anything to help me, other than trying to keep my mind occupied. I had not expected the pain to be that bad; I was not expecting any of it at all. The nurse explained, "It's your body going into early labour, just like how it would happen during childbirth. All you can do is wait for the tissue to pass."

For hours, I sat in agony. Every so often, Chantal would rub my back while I was bent over, trying to help me relax. She also tried to comfort me with her inharmonious rendition of Stevie Wonder's 'Happy Birthday'. As amazing as she was, it didn't help; it just became background noise as I fought it through.

Sitting on the toilet was where I felt the most comfort. I was exhausted. I was bleeding heavily, followed by a lot of clots, big and small.

I asked the nurse, "Have I already passed the foetal tissue?"

To which she responded with a laugh. "No, you will

know once you have."

I felt puzzled, not knowing what to expect. Around thirty minutes later, I felt the eleven-week-old foetal tissue withdraw from my body. I couldn't help myself; I sat staring at it. The nurse was correct. I knew once I saw it. What I had passed was surprisingly big and quite solid. It had already held the shape and formation of a baby. It was an image I would never forget, permanently imprinted into my mind. I sat in silence for ages, just examining the head. I could also see where the arms and legs were beginning to form; he was curled in a foetal position— covered in a blood-soaked mucous, my baby. I pondered for a while and shed a few private tears. I didn't want to let my baby go, and though it may not have been fully grown, I still loved him no less than I would any other. I picked him up and placed him in a sterile container; this was to be collected from the nurse for further investigation.

I was kept in overnight to ensure everything went well. Grayson and Chantal had to leave at eight due to visiting hours. No one was allowed to stay with me despite having a private room. I slept little that evening, even as the pain subsided.

Grayson returned in the morning at nine; I had another scan to check all was clear and okay. Then we sat in the room together, waiting to be discharged. I just laid in bed. The TV was on in the background, just general daytime shows. I was not feeling great at all. I still felt exhausted from the previous night, mentally and physically. Grayson and I sat talking, trying to keep my mind busy and distracting ourselves from everything that had just happened.

"I could be working right now, earning money instead of sitting here with you," Grayson said out of nowhere. I turned to face him, stunned at what I had just heard. After everything I have been through, I never expected to hear such brash words from him. I was in disbelief. My heart, already broken from losing our baby, cracked open wider at his tactless words. Was his work really more important than his baby and me? I couldn't comprehend it at all. He had never said anything like that before; he was always so considerate, and so it was unexpected.

Even when we returned to being happy and enjoying spending our time together, in the back of my mind, I never forgot what he said. I knew it wouldn't be easy to forgive. Someone saying something so inconsiderate at one of the most distressing times of my life tends to stick in my head. The feelings also remained, I just tried to ignore it.

The whole situation was a true test on our relationship. It was my first time pregnant, so it was my first time experiencing a pregnancy and loss all at once. I was finally discharged at one o'clock, and it was like I'd never even been pregnant. All that was left was an empty void inside me. One moment I was excited and planning for a baby, and the next, it had all disappeared. It happened too quickly, yet that was all the time needed for me to fall in love with my baby.

I decided that after all that ordeal, I needed to escape for a few days. Grayson didn't mind me going away. I assumed he needed time to think about things, just like

I did. I thought having time apart to think alone would help; we were both hurting, and with that came the risk of one of us saying something we may regret.

With the way I felt, I knew I had to get away instantly, to mask the pain. I contacted my friend Neil who lived in Toronto. We had known each other since 1996. I met Neil back when I was living in the Philippines, and when I left to move back to the UK, he moved to Canada. Even though we had distance between us, thanks to social media, we never lost contact and remained close friends.

In Canada, Neil picked me up from the airport and hosted me at his mum's house in Mississauga. Her house was welcoming from the moment that the door opened. It was unpretentious and old-fashioned, with many photographs of children, so obviously loved. The hallway led to an aged, grand, wooden staircase, which led upstairs to several rooms. This was to be my home for the next four days. I have always found it interesting to experience the lifestyle of those living abroad.

Neil showed me around Toronto. As we drove around, there was a freezing chill in the air, helped by the effect of Lake Ontario. The weather didn't bother me, though; the wintry sun was still bright and beaming through the grey clouds. I was enjoying life in a metropolitan city. Within the impressive skyline stood the CN tower, shooting straight up. I took many photos, before we moved on to the quirky backstreets. There was an antique market with plenty of buskers and wandering musicians – this was very much a multicultural city.

The following day, Neil surprised me with a trip to Niagara Falls. He had booked the Marriott Fallsview Hotel for the evening. Upon checking into the room, I was amazed by the exceptional view overlooking one of nature's wonders. I stood mesmerised by the beauty of three sets of waterfalls: Horseshoe Falls, Bridal Veil Falls, and the American Falls. The falls were set on the Niagara River; this river connects Lake Erie with Lake Ontario (two of the five great lakes).

Suddenly, I understood why Neil had booked this hotel. As dusk fell, Niagara Falls illuminated and transformed this beautiful water wonder into a kaleidoscopic cascade of colours. As if that wasn't enough, there were also spectacular fireworks lighting up the sky, and I watched in awe.

This was why the world was such a beautiful place. It was one reason I loved travelling: the ability to witness with my own eyes the beauty of our planet. Too many people go through life believing they have their eyes open yet miss the beauty that surrounds them. I didn't want to be one of them.

After dark, we headed over to the Vegas-vibe casinos. And after a few hours of trying to go for gold, we worked up an appetite. We made our way towards the local diner.

The waiter approached us, "What would you like to order?"

I couldn't resist the menu, "A stack of blueberry pancakes in Canadian maple syrup with a large chocolate milkshake please."

It all looked amazing; for some reason, the food seemed to taste so much better than back home.

The Canadian side of Niagara was packed with shops, casinos, and buzzing nightlife. Looking out past the falls, I could see acres of lush greenery. This side, you could lay eyes on an entire panoramic view of all three falls.

We crossed over into New York state to observe the falls from the other side. There, we joined the Maid of the Mist tour, a small boat ride into the midst of the waterfalls. After, we eyeballed the falls from the observation tower and other viewing areas in the park; it was strange to view the waterfalls from this low perspective. However, to be that close to the grandeur of the falls and being surrounded with acres of the landscape was indeed the experience of a lifetime.

My journey to Canada and spending time with an old friend was just what I needed – Neil was accommodating and very sympathetic about what had happened. He tried to keep me entertained and keep my mind occupied while I was there. But sometimes I know that I seemed unaware of the outside world, pondering my thoughts. Even so, the whole trip was incredible, and one I will never forget.

I spoke to Grayson every day while I was away, and he seemed fine: chirpy, happy and genuinely interested when I told him what I had been up to. Nothing seemed to have changed between us, and he certainly did not indicate any issues.

The night before I was due to fly back home, I was messaging to Grayson. He texted, "I'll be collecting you from the airport. You should wait for me at the terminal near the Virgin Atlantic check-in point at Heathrow."

"Thank you," I replied. I followed it up with; "Even though I had a wonderful experience in Toronto and I'm grateful for the time Neil took to show me around, I am ready to go home. This break has helped me clear my head. I've missed you alot and can't wait to see you."

Guy Fawkes Day, a day that I remember perfectly. It was the day I was due to fly home. It was pitch black during my arrival. I was smiling as the plane was coming into land. As I looked out the window from above, the sky was filled with exploding lights and colours from thousands of firework celebrations. I switched on my phone as I waited anxiously for the announcement that the plane was parked, and it was safe to leave the aircraft.

My phone beeped; I had received a text from Grayson. Excitedly, I opened it, expecting it to read, "I'm here."

Instead, it said, "I have ordered you a cab to take you straight home to your flat."

My phone beeped again, a follow-up message, "While you have been away, it has given me time to think, and I have decided that I don't want to have any more children, and I don't think we should be together anymore."

It didn't make sense; after all we'd been through; he broke things off with me via a text message.

I arrived at my flat. Alone. Cars would pass by my window, and I would flinch at everyone, thinking it was Grayson. I couldn't understand why he had left me or what I had done wrong. If anything, I felt like I rightfully earned an explanation and without one I felt left in the dark. I repeatedly went back to the house. I texted and called him, but he didn't answer. I demanded an explanation – something had to have happened while I was away, something that Grayson, for some strange reason, wasn't telling me. Finally, I drove to his house and knocked on his door. Grayson opened it, staring at me with cool, lost, empty eyes. "I've met someone else younger, I like her a lot, and I want to keep seeing her."

His words caused my heart to freeze and then shatter. Although it was a relief to finally have an explanation, he had been lying and leading me astray the whole time I was out of the country. While he was drinking in a nightclub, Grayson had met a girl in her early twenties. He said he had been thinking and that he had decided that he didn't want to have any more children. He was happy with just having Brandon, he assumed I was at the age where I wanted to settle down and have kids. *Why didn't he think to talk with me first?*

Does the truth imprison us, *or does it set us free?* One thing is for sure: the truth can hurt. I never expected his words to hurt so much. I felt the hot tears welling up in my eyes, and I could tell he regretted every word he said, but we both knew his words were the truth.

two

MOVING FORWARD

THE WORD 'EX-BOYFRIEND' ALONE was enough to make me choke. In my dreams, we were going to start a family; now, he was my ex, and I was supposed to be okay with that. Just move on and forget, like it didn't matter. I couldn't do that; it hurt me more than it hurt him.

Everyone said, "Time heals all wounds. You'll move on when you find someone new." Meanwhile, my heartache was turning into hatred.

Thankfully, I had little time to dwell; I was looking forward to travelling to Budapest to celebrate my friend Aimee's birthday. She had just turned twenty-one. Aimee and I had been good friends since we met working together for the USA travel company. We trained alongside each other, and we shared a lot of giggles whilst in each other's company.

Travelling to Budapest were a few girls from the office: Aimee, Sara, Lisa, Emma, and about six more of Aimee's closest friends and myself. We spent three nights in Budapest at the centrally located and stylish Atrium Fashion Hotel. Our hotel's lobby was more like the reception of a new high-rise. Small and bland, it was also light and airy, with only one staff member in sight. The walls were bright, with eye-catching colours.

On our first evening, we put on our dancing shoes and stepped into a bar, it was dark and overcrowded, with hundreds of conversations being held in loud voices, all competing with the music. As the night progressed, I became drunk quickly. The evening was full of easy conversation, laughter and smiles, and the cheap spirits. The following evening, we booked a meal. We were a group of young women full of helpless giggles. As I looked around at the busy tables, there was an old couple eating side by side, holding a glass of wine each, and a family and their children. The children's noise level was high, but it didn't bother me, I was enjoying myself.

It was the beginning of the Christmas season, and what better way to start it than to go to Disney World in sunny Florida? My spirits were lifted. I had started to move on from Grayson. My break to Budapest with friends had helped. Aimee accompanied me on the six-day magical journey to Florida. It was a jam-packed mega familiarisation trip with a hundred other travel agents, and a crammed schedule.

Our mornings began with breakfast at 6am. Disney's Boardwalk Inn hosted us for the first three nights. Our hotel was set on a turn-of-the-century Coney Island-style boardwalk surrounded by a shimmering crescent lake. It was within walking distance to Epcot and Disney's Hollywood Studios.

The first few days were filled with thrills at the theme parks, SeaWorld, and swimming with dolphins. We also visited Aquatica and Blizzard Beach, which were the most relaxing of the water parks. We had several cocktail evenings and watched firework displays.

For the second part of the trip, we stayed at the Loews Portofino Bay Hotel, inspired by the beauty, romance, and charm of the seaside village of Portofino, Italy. This latter part of the trip included riding Everglade airboats, nightly shows such as the Blue Man Group and driving out to experience the Animal Kingdom.

I remembered one evening; Aimee and I were both so tired that Aimee didn't even make it to her bed. As the door swung open, she dropped to the floor and fell asleep there.

The purpose of our trip was to experience the parks and hotels so that it was easier to sell them. The company believed that to sell products to the best of our abilities, we needed to know how it felt to be there, and it would make it easier for us to confirm bookings if we could share our own experience with our customers.

Back home, everything went back to normal, though I began to feel lonely. With all the trips over and Christmas approaching rapidly, I felt lost and stuck in a rut. I wanted to find something to do, so I signed up to a dating website. I wanted to be able to chat with someone. I wasn't planning on dating; I just wanted to find companionship, someone who didn't know me personally. I wanted to be someone else and to forget the life I had once. Online, I could speak to unfamiliar people who did not know my story, nor my past. I just wanted to be able to be me again, not the girl who had just lost her baby and her partner.

On the dating app, I started talking to one guy, who seemed nice. But I didn't feel compelled to take it further; I knew I would never meet him, but talking to him online was fine.

Then I went on a date with an old school friend, Scott. He had been in the year above me in high school. I had seen him around. We had mutual friends, and he sometimes drank near where I lived. I felt obliged to go on a date with him simply because we knew each other. He was not my cup of tea, but I would have felt embarrassed, turning him down, knowing I would be bumping into him occasionally.

On the night of our date, I felt awkward. There was no initial attraction whatsoever on my side, although I thought I would give him the benefit of the doubt and see how the conversation flowed before rushing to a conclusion.

He had booked a local Italian restaurant for dinner, and upon entering the restaurant, I noted dim lighting, scuffed walls, and Banksy-inspired art. Scott was polite but annoyingly overconfident. I didn't feel comfortable at all on the date, as it just didn't feel natural, and I felt like I was forcing the whole thing. We enjoyed the meal, and even though I enjoyed the company, I just wasn't ready to date anyone, or maybe he just was not the right one.

Sara, my friend who sat next to me at work, would notice every time Scott emailed me, as I would be slightly plagued. Besides emailing me, he would constantly call my direct line, and text me– he was generally becoming a nuisance. I needed some space as I was trying to think of a nice way to tell him I didn't want to see him anymore; I also didn't want to lead him on. He knew I was at work yet continued to badger me. Sara could also see I had no interest – she was right. He was very pushy, and when I stopped replying to him for a while, he messaged me again.

He said, "You should just tell me if you don't want to see me anymore." So, I did just that; it was for the best.

On the dating website, I didn't post a profile picture of myself, because I wanted to remain anonymous. It was just a way to talk to someone without being judged. Even without a photo, many men were happy to chat, and I enjoyed talking with them.

I didn't do it to forget about the baby I lost. I did it to forget about the heartache that came with it. I wanted to escape the concerned looks from those who knew what had happened and the endless sympathy. It was like a secret life, one that helped me move forward. I didn't have to explain to anyone that I was okay, that I had lost a baby, or that my partner had left me. We spoke about work, hobbies, travelling. I avoided sharing anything too personal with them.

One evening after work, I browsed through the profiles to see if anyone sparked an interest. My eyes landed on a guy dressed in a crisp white work shirt and skinny black tie. His facial features were babyish; he had small, chestnut brown eyes and olive skin. He had broad shoulders with short brown hair and two deep dimples. There was nothing rugged about his looks; even his jaw was shaved smooth. I had always been attracted to the bad boy type before and was surprised to find myself attracted to this guy. However, I felt drawn to him; he felt safe. Intrigued, I sent him a little online quiz, and to my surprise, he took the time to fill it out. I sent him a message afterward, and from then, we started exchanging messages. He was different, and I needed different in my life. His name was Michael or Mike for short. He seemed friendly and cute and had a quote on his profile: "Life is like photography. We develop from the negative."

His quote helped me reflect on what I was going through at that moment in my life. I was curious to learn more about him.

Soon, speaking to Mike online became the highlight of my day, and I could not stop myself from wanting to get to know him more. Our conversations were always light-hearted; we were always getting along. I found him very self-contained and private. He would only let me know what he wanted me to know. I constantly counted down the hours at work until nightfall so that I could check if he had sent me another message. I was hooked and, of course, he had messaged me; we exchanged messages every night. After speaking online for a whole month, I found out about his family, friends and work life.

Mike appeared to be very down to earth, thoughtful, well educated, and generally kind-hearted. He was confident, yet not an egotist or smug. He seemed like the type of man I wanted in my life. He was living with friends in Blackfriars, although he was originally from South London. He was working at a bank in London Bridge.

The first month of exchanging messages was amazing, but he had not yet asked to meet nor for my number. I this found odd – most guys by the end of the first week would have asked for my number, saying they found it easier to talk over the phone than the website. I began to worry. My mind was conjuring up all kinds of scenarios. What if it was not him? His picture might be a fake; I could be getting catfished. I now saw him as a close friend, and by meeting, I could potentially lose that friendship if he didn't act the same way he did online. He had been my rock throughout the month; it was amazing how fast you could get to know someone when you are on the same wavelength.

I was overthinking everything. Would I be able to look past his lies and still sit and talk to him if he wasn't the same man from the picture? I would be alone again if anything were to go wrong; I didn't want to risk that. I considered keeping our relationship online, but I just knew that if I met him, and he was real, things could be so much better. I just had to take the risk and hope he was real.

My birthday was quickly approaching. I had made plans to celebrate with friends at Abacus, a nightclub in London. I decided it was the perfect opportunity to invite Mike and finally meet him. After all, it was in a public place with the benefit of safety in numbers. I would have my friends there with me, and if we didn't hit it off, he could stay, have a drink and possibly meet someone else.

I invited him and told him to feel free to bring a couple of friends. I didn't want to feel the pressure of looking after him. I had concerns that he wasn't as interested in me as I was in him. I was fed up with waiting for him to ask me out, although he could have just been waiting for what he felt like was the right time. Maybe he avoided asking in case he scared me off, or maybe he just had the same concerns I did. But even so, I was more afraid he wasn't as interested in me as I thought he was.

However, Mike did agree to a meeting up, and that helped me to relax more. Surely, he wouldn't agree to meet me if he wasn't who he said he was?

The much-awaited night of my birthday had arrived. I was nervous all night, mainly because I didn't want to be disappointed. I spent a lot of time around friends having fun. But I found my eyes constantly looking towards the entrance. I was in the lower part of the club, it was dark, and the music was blaring. We were all dancing and enjoying ourselves; there wasn't much signal on my phone, but I didn't want to ignore my friends by constantly checking for him either. I went to the bar, to order a drink, and as I turned around, I saw a guy walking up the stairs. He looked just like Mike's profile photo. I had a tummy full of fluttering butterflies.

I shouted, "Mike."

He turned, and his smile melted me. He looked down towards me and replied, "Colette?"

We started chatting; his voice was more inviting than a half-price shoe sale! He came downstairs with me, we ordered a drink, danced and chatted.

Chantal was studying at a university a few hours away at the time but made it down to celebrate with me. I hoped she would like Mike. I only had one sister, and it was important that whomever I dated would get along with her too.

She met him and studied him under lowered eyes. She had noticed that he differed from all the other men I had dated in the past, and she liked that he was different. So, did I. They got along well, and she thought he was a nice guy.

I was instantly hooked by his wit and charm. He was easy to get on with, and I felt like I had known him for ages. All too fast, it was time for me to leave. I needed to catch the last train, as I had work the following morning. Before I left, we exchanged numbers.

As I reached the train station, I said to my friend Lisa, "I want to go back inside. I don't want the night to end."

I was on cloud nine. She quickly reminded me, "Well, you have an early start in the morning."

When I got home that evening, my feet were hurting from wearing stiletto heels, and my head was spinning from drinking too much alcohol. I was tired, but I felt terrific.

After an hour, my phone rang. I didn't recognise the number, and so, hesitantly, I picked up the phone. It was Mike calling me for the first time; he was also intoxicated and had just arrived home. We chatted for a while; it felt strange speaking to him on the phone– things were progressing. I felt like I was cheating on online Mike by talking to real Mike in person.

"Do you want to meet up tomorrow?" he asked me.

I wasn't sure at first. It wasn't what I would usually do. Generally, I avoided going out after work. I wanted to see him, though, so I said, "Yes."

We set a time to meet at a bar called Hungerford House on the Embankment. I couldn't believe it!

The following day felt like it went on forever. I was sleep-deprived and hung-over; I had to work for the whole day, and then I had committed to going on a date.

Finally, I made my way to Hungerford House, and Mike met me there; we greeted each other at the bar and kissed cheek to cheek. The bar was empty. It was still early on a Saturday night. We ordered some drinks and snacks. Sitting down at a table close to a window, we began to chat. I noticed that he seemed calmer and refreshed, maybe because he didn't have to go to work that day! The night was still young.

We were drinking and chatting away when a homeless guy approached us. The poor guy was dressed in rags, and needed a good shower. He was covered in dirt and smelled of dried urine. I gave him some money, hoping he would walk off, but instead, he tried talking to us.

"Sorry, would you be able to leave us alone? We are discussing our wedding plans," Mike was looking at the man as he asked him respectfully.

I nearly choked on my drink, hearing his words. I knew that he was confident, but I was thrown back by that comment. He was very amicable; I assumed most people would have just been rude and told him to go away and leave us alone. I was so impressed.

We ended up bar hopping and enjoying the London night. He was pleasant and good-natured. Not once did I feel uncomfortable with him. Besides another moment where we were dancing in a bar, and he got down on his knees, the people in the bar were laughing at my embarrassment. Mike was a bit of a showman. He wasn't fazed about what people may think, whereas I would cringe and want the ground to swallow me up.

Mike was my complete opposite, but, from there, we began dating. I had planned to spend Valentine's Day with my mum in Iceland. I had planned it before I even met Mike online; when I booked it, I didn't want to be in the UK for Valentine's. Dating was going well, and Mike was fine with me going abroad over Valentine's. The morning I was due to be flying out, Mike had left the house early and texted me, "Check under your pillow." Underneath, I found a Valentine's card. Discovering that he had made the sweet gesture left me a little disheartened that I would be away.

In Iceland, the hotel my mum and I stayed in was horrific. The room was far too small, and it had just two single beds, a dressing table and a wardrobe attached to it. There was about a foot between the bed and the dresser, and we had to climb over our bags to move around.

One evening, we were getting ready to go on the Northern Lights tour. I was speaking to my mum about Mike. I was telling her about how much I liked him. "I should ask him if he wants to come to the Philippines," I said without really thinking.

My mum is Filipino, and my father is British, although I was born and raised in the UK after I finished high school I took a gap year, which lead me to residing in Manila for the next five years.

During these younger years, around 1996, I worked as a runway, commercial and print model. In 1998, I went on to be a candidate in one of the nation's biggest beauty pageants, Miss Philippines (aka Binibining Pilipinas). During the competition, I won the minor titles: Miss Lux Super Rich (for my long hair) and Best in Swimsuit. I then went on to becoming a major titleholder: Miss

Philippines International.

The major title allowed me to represent the Philippines in Japan at the Miss International competition. Unfortunately, due to my age (I was seventeen at the time), I could not win either of the other titles, which would allow me to compete in one of the two remaining big international beauty pageants: Miss World and Miss Universe.

We all know the stigma: the drop-dead gorgeous woman with the rock-solid body who struts her stuff in her bikini. She is practically a goddess in her evening gown. You swear her makeup is tattooed on her face because it is just too perfect. Followed by those on-stage questions, the immediate answer that crosses everyone's mind… "World peace." When people think of beauty pageants, they get a certain mental image based on what they have seen from watching them on TV and from stories in the news. However, most people don't understand what these pageants are like from the perspective of participating in them.

It is true; you are groomed to be skinny, have perfect teeth, perfect skin and the perfect body. However, before my competition, I had intense training in posture, the catwalk, stage presence, wardrobe and styling, interview preparation and techniques, self-development, hair, and make-up advice, speaking, reading, writing and listening in Japanese, etiquette, and I also had a personal trainer every day.

During the last month, I wasn't able to socialise or see anyone besides my trainers. I had to reside in a room based inside the Araneta Coliseum and stick to my intense training program; it was hard work, to say the least. There is a big misconception regarding these competitions. There were benefits from competing. Some that I took from my beauty queen days were personal development, communication skills, confidence, and handling the pressure and disappointments in life. It was an extremely daunting and a very pressurising experience. When you stood up on that stage, you laid your eyes on thousands of people fixated on you, blinded by flashing lights, judged on every move you make, and that was just the start. Representing the country while I was still very young taught me to grow up quickly, to be independent, and stay strong, no matter my encounters.

I was placed in the top ten that year, and the Miss International title was won by Miss Panama. Overall, I lived under the limelight for five years. The Miss Philippines competition opened up a lot of doors for me. I co-hosted two of my own TV shows, I was invited to guest on other programs, and I participated in runway shows in many cities worldwide.

My mum and I were planning to tour around Asia for three weeks. I try to visit my friends and relatives every year. Part of me was joking when I messaged Mike, "Do you want to come to the Philippines with me?"

I didn't even know if he liked me that much and inviting him on holiday already seemed too much too soon. After all, we had only been dating a month. I was infatuated with him, though, and it felt like I had known him for ages. I texted him anyway, partly nervous and partly excited, I closed my eyes and pressed the send button. To my surprise, Mike responded quickly and seemed unfazed. He asked me, "What flights have you booked coming home? And what are the dates and timings?"

Eagerly, I asked my mum, "What are our flight details?" Then, I enthusiastically messaged him back.

"All done, I've booked," he replied.

Not even an hour had passed since I had messaged him the flight details. Dumbfounded, I didn't know what to do.

"Mum, he's booked his flights, now what? I didn't think he would do it." Looking at my mum, I really hadn't expected him to say yes, but he was now coming to the Philippines.

"Well, you invited him, you will have to show him around the islands." My mum just laughed at me; her reply was not much help in easing my worries.

During this time I had resigned from my job at the USA travel company for an opportunity to become an assistant manager at a local high street travel agency. I had always dreamed of having my own company. I am very ambitious and I felt that making the job change would help me to move up the career ladder.

March rapidly approached, and it was time for our big Asia tour. My mum and I travelled through Thailand, Cambodia, Singapore, Hong Kong, and Nepal, and during each visit, I was always looking around to find access to the Internet. I was in constant contact with Mike, updating him with what I was seeing and doing. Due to the time difference, I would usually email him at night and get a response by the morning.

Finally, on the last leg of the journey, I flew on to the Philippines, where I was due to meet Mike. When he arrived in Manila, I picked him up from the airport. At first it was slightly awkward. I didn't know how to act around him, and the whole situation was surreal. I had butterflies and was excited; yet I was nervous about the situation, as I wasn't yet 100% about him. We travelled to an island just off Manila called Boracay, where we took a charter flight and a boat ride to the small island.

A powdery-white sand beach, clear turquoise water, and blazing heat. The island had many dining choices, bars, and nightlife and water sports. Boracay had always been one of my favourite destinations, so much so that I had written my dissertation on the eco-life of the island. Mike had never travelled to Asia before and was pleasantly surprised. We had a lot of fun, and it wasn't as daunting as I first anticipated.

Shortly after our return home from the holiday, Mike's contract for the house he was renting was ending. His only option, due to money, was to move back to his parents' house in South London.

"You should move in with me," I said.

At the time, I was living alone, and I knew that Mike moving in was a big step. If it worked, it would be amazing.

"I will," he agreed, and then, he moved in. It was perfect.

During this time things weren't going as well as expected at work. My manager was a secret alcoholic sufferer. I would find bottles of Vodka hidden in the cupboards and drawers, at first it wasn't that obvious, then some mornings I would find that he had left the shop unlocked and was asleep behind the desks. If I tried speaking to him all his words would be slurred.

I worked there for around 3 months, it turned out that he would take payment for holidays from customers and not book them or sometimes he would book them a one way ticket. One day my manager just disappeared, I didn't get paid for my last month and there were a lot of angry customers. Luckily, I had help from a girl called Hayley who had been working with me for a couple of months. We didn't want to leave holidaymakers stranded, and tried to fix what we could. Hayley and I were oblivious to the situation just like everyone else. The next few weeks were difficult as we had a lot of threats from customers and local bystanders. The press would keep returning for updates and bailiffs came in to slowly collect items in the shop. Not only was he scheming people he was also in a lot of debt. Over the course of a couple of weeks, the shop was emptied and finally closed. I was now unemployed.

To keep me occupied I helped my parents run their properties.

One day my father asked me if I was capable of running and owning my own travel company. Honestly,

I didn't have the confidence. However, I knew whatever I answered at this point I wouldn't be able to go back on. With my father you get one shot and I knew that it was an opportunity I couldn't pass up, I smiled and replied, "Yes Dad, of course I could".

November 2009 marked the date I opened my own travel agency. I felt privileged to have been given this opportunity by my father; he was willing to invest in my dream, having a business was hard work and I had a lot to learn.

After eight months of dating, I finally went with Mike to South London to meet his family. It was one of the scariest things; because it was an important step for us, or it is that we always pressure ourselves because we want to create the right first impression.

His parents, Clive and Susan, were so welcoming. I became engrossed in conversations that helped ease my nerves. I was very fond of them. They differed from most parents I had met; they grew their own fruit and vegetables in their allotment at the back of their garden. They made home-cooked meals and produced their own jams and chutneys. Mike was just like his parents: altruistic and warm-hearted. I enjoyed visiting them; they were very supportive of us, which made me feel at ease.

three

NOT MY TIME

THE NEXT YEAR, THINGS progressed quickly. I was engrossed with my business, and Mike was active with his work, however, we always found time for minibreaks and "us." Our relationship had grown stronger, and, like all couples, we had our issues but never anything we could not solve together. I was feeling happy and complacent with the direction things were heading.

August 2010, I was alone, pondering. My period was late, and I had a strange feeling in the pit of my stomach. I sat in my tiny bathroom; it felt like déjà vu, I had been here once before a couple of years ago. My hands were shaking as I took a test. Although Mike and

I had 'not been trying,' I was hoping to see a positive pregnancy result. I patiently waited, staring at the window of the pregnancy test. It felt like at least half an hour had passed as I anxiously waited for the results. I checked my watch; the three minutes were finally over, and, taking a deep breath, I picked up the pregnancy test.

The two visible red lines looked back at me – yes! The result was positive.

I couldn't help but smile, my heart pounding full of excitement, worry, and shock. There were so many nerves residing inside of me, but mostly I was happy. Thinking you might be pregnant, and having it confirmed were two different things. In a flash, everything had changed. Although I knew that every pregnancy was different, I tried not to let my previous experience alter how I was feeling. My past had educated me, and I was now much more aware of the complications and risks.

I waited for Mike to finish work, and when he came walking through the door that night, I showed him the test. We then sat on the sofa; eagerly, I watched him, waiting to gauge his reaction. He was happy; it was clear he was, but just like me, he was a little nervous as well. I had felt like it was the right time for me before, but it clearly was not. But now, with Mike, it was the perfect time for us to have a baby together. Mike knew about what had happened to me previously, so despite being pleased, his happiness was masked with apprehension.

I was overjoyed thinking about being pregnant again, and it felt different with Mike; he was dependable and acted more responsibly. I knew at this point, I was with the right person. The first six weeks flew by quickly; we decided we would tell his parents in person.

We wanted to share the good news. I was a little more hesitant than Mike; it was still early days, I didn't want to tell everyone in case something went wrong, and we would have to go back and afflict them by telling them that the baby was gone.

After having lunch, we were all sitting down in the kitchen at Mike's parents' house. We told them together, and his mum leaped up with a yelp, followed by instant tears of joy; this had a knock-on effect, and Mike began to well up when he saw how thrilled his mum was. In return, I was tearful seeing how happy they all were. Although his dad seemed more reserved, he was also upbeat; they were both over the moon upon hearing the news.

We told my sister and her boyfriend at the time, Bobby; they were both delighted and supportive. My sister was controlling her joy, as she had seen first-hand what had happened to me previously and was being cautious. Chantal was very much like me and loved children. In her spare time, she would babysit, and she had previously worked in the local infant school.

I couldn't settle. I kept feeling anxious. I couldn't erase the memory of what happened last time. I wanted to treat this pregnancy differently, and not let the last one have a hold on me, but it was in the back of my mind, no matter how much I tried to ignore it.

It was a week later, both sets of parents now knew

about the pregnancy. I was at work, when I started spotting. I just knew instantly that it was not a good sign but tried to remain positive and calm. I called Mike and told him the situation; I advised him I was going to the EPU (Early Pregnancy Unit).

I stepped foot in the familiar hospital corridor it was stuffy, the air had an underlying aroma of bleach, and the walls were painted in magnolia and were scraped in places from all the hundreds of trolleys that had bumped into them. The pictures on the walls were cheap prints of uplifting scenes. However, they didn't uplift my spirits. Just above the double doors were large plastic signs pointing to the different hospital departments. I arrived at the EPU unaccompanied. I was contemplating what the outcome would be. Around thirty to forty percent of pregnancies ended in miscarriages. My gut instinct was telling me that mine would be one, but I tried to remain hopeful.

I waited for Mike to arrive from work; he came straight to the hospital to meet me, I was pleased to see him. From across the corridor, he smiled at me, and gave me a little wave. He walked towards me and gave me a kiss and a cuddle. We sat down together.

"How are you feeling?" he asked me.

I looked up at him. "I don't know; I don't know what to expect," I replied and took a breath. "I don't understand why this is happening to me again."

We chatted for a few minutes; he tried to reassure me while we waited to be called into the scan room.

A lady came out and called my name; Mike

chaperoned me into the room. I was asked a few routine questions, including, "Why did you come in today?".

I explained my history and that I had started to spot, and that I wanted to get it double-checked. This time, because I was at a much earlier stage of the pregnancy, I had to have a trans-vaginal scan. They wouldn't normally be able to detect a heartbeat at this stage, but they can check the size of the gestational sac and the location of the pregnancy. She smiled at me and asked me to undress from the waist down.

This time, I was lying in a more upright position with my knees up and my feet in stirrups. She placed a long piece of tissue over the lower part of my body and grabbed an ultrasound probe; it was the approximate size of two fingers and shaped like a wand. Next, she placed a sterile latex condom over it, followed by a dollop of cold lubricating gel, and inserted it into my vagina. This was slightly discomforting as she rotated it, moving it from side to side. The probe was transmitting information to the computer, which was placed to the right and away from me. I was observing her facial expressions closely; I wanted to see if she would give me any hints. I glanced over at Mike, who was also focused on the screen. His face was blank. I knew he couldn't understand what he was looking at.

As I looked back at the sonographer, her face dropped. I sensed instantly that something was wrong; she looked demoralised. She turned to us and tried to give a sympathetic smile.

"I'm sorry. Unfortunately, there isn't a heartbeat." She

paused briefly. "By the gestation size, a heartbeat should have already developed." My heart sank faster than a penny in a pond. Was I even breathing? Every thought in my mind was silenced into denial and grief.

She guided us back through the dull, beige, tiled hallway and out into the waiting area. We had to stick around for some paperwork to be typed up. When we were handed it, we had to walk over to the wing of the hospital where I waited a couple of years ago with Stef. The dark cloud of gloom was shadowing me as we walked through the hospital, the smell of illness and death in the air. The older part of the hospital had an eerie feel, which always made me feel uncomfortable. It was a long walk in silence.

Once we were called into the consulting room, the doctor explained that I had miscarried once again and reiterated this was normal. I didn't believe him. I was adamant that something was wrong. He prescribed Misoprostol after perusing my notes; he said it had worked for me previously, so he wanted me to use them again. He explained that my baby would miscarry within a week. I didn't need to be admitted this time, because the foetus was smaller than previously, therefore, the medication should work. I kept asking myself if it was something I had done that had caused it. Of course, they say it just happens, but it does not stop the thoughts of what if?

The whole week I stayed at home – I couldn't think about work, and just like before, the cramps were causing discomfort. Both Mike and I were worried about if I miscarried while I was out of the house. It also felt safer at home, rather than having to risk bumping into people I would know.

Mike called his parents and explained over the phone what had happened. I could overhear the conversation, but I was numb. This would have been their first grandchild. I could hear their lowered voices and tears of sadness. I felt guilty. I knew that it wasn't my fault, but to feel the pressure of crushing someone else's dreams was heart-breaking for me. It was comforting to know that I wasn't alone and that I had support, but it didn't change how I was feeling.

Part of me wondered if the next stage was for Mike to break up with me. Was I repeating history? I could see he was really upset; I felt awful for him. I had been through this before, I had experienced the rollercoaster of emotions, and knew what to expect, but for Mike, it was the first time. He would be struggling to understand all the emotions that just hit you and he would have to figure out how to deal with his feeling of grief.

I had a trip planned; I was meant to be flying out to Sardinia for an educational. I didn't want to cancel the trip, but after a week I still hadn't miscarried. I went back to Whipps Cross to find out what would happen next.

Back at the hospital, I spoke to the doctor and explained that the tablets did not have a reaction. Both the doctor and I thought it would have worked as it did last time. Unfortunately, this wasn't the case.

The doctor then said, "You'll need to cancel the trip

to Sardinia. You will need to have an operation."

This upset me; I was looking forward to the trip, but I could not leave England without having the operation and risk being sick abroad. He explained I was at risk of catching an infection due to not miscarrying. He asked me a few questions about my past miscarriage and requested to use the foetus for medical experiments and testing after extraction. We agreed and had to sign consent forms. I was told that I would be having a dilation and curettage operation, also known as a D&C. It is a process whereby they dilate the cervix and surgically remove part of the lining of the uterus and the contents by scraping and scooping.

I was given a date to return to the hospital as they could not admit me there and then; they did not want to leave it any longer than necessary, so the appointment was in two days. I was told I would have to fast from midnight the night before the operation. This was because I would be under general anaesthetic.

A couple of days later Mike and I went to the Plane Tree Centre at Whipps Cross Hospital. I was shown to a room; it was private like last time, just a lot smaller. It had a reclining armchair to the right of the bed. I was sat waiting for hours. I was so hungry I felt faint; the nurse put me on an IV drip. I walked around the halls, trying to pass the time.

I was surprised to see a friend lying on a ward bed, I spoke to her, unsure of why she was in the hospital. I found out that she had suffered from an ectopic pregnancy. I didn't know exactly what an ectopic pregnancy was. She explained that it is when a fertilised egg implants itself outside of the womb, usually in one of the fallopian tubes. Unfortunately, it doesn't develop into a baby and needs to be surgically removed I had no idea she was even pregnant, I had seen her just a few days earlier. I could understand why she would keep it a secret, though; we exchanged a few words, and I carried on wandering around.

I was eventually scheduled for the procedure late in the evening. Mike wasn't permitted to accompany me, so he waited in the room until I returned.

Post-operation, I was moved back to my room. I felt strange. I didn't feel pregnant anymore, yet the pain was still there from losing the baby. A nurse kept entering the room, checking my blood pressure and pulse to ensure I was safe and fit to go home. After eating a sandwich and going to the toilet without incident, she seemed happy to discharge me.

She said, "Wear sanitary pads for the bleeding. You need to rest for a few days, so you probably need to take time off of work." I did so and rested.

Doctors and nurses repeatedly told me that it was common for women to miscarry and that even having two miscarriages was normal. I just felt like something did not sit right with me, and I wanted to see a specialist about it. When I asked the doctor, I was surprised to be told that it was not possible; they would only allow me to see a specialist after I had three miscarriages or could not conceive after trying for two years. I was amazed; I could not believe that the NHS would let people go through all the pain and hurt I had suffered, not once but three times before even considering looking into if they had an infertility problem. I didn't understand why they would make someone wait two years before addressing their issues. It felt like precious time was being wasted. I had no choice but to accept it, though. I had to wait. I just hoped that when I fell pregnant again without complications, and that I wouldn't need to go through the process of being referred.

After my operation, time passed quickly. I concentrated a lot more on my business because I wanted it to be a success. Mike and I travelled abroad frequently during this period. We visited Miami, Goa, Portugal, and a few other destinations. Mike didn't seem as worried as I was about conceiving; he seemed to cope well with everything, which meant he was amazing at supporting me. Every day I didn't have a baby affected me. A baby was all I wanted. I was determined to have one, but I continued to try and keep myself occupied. When I walked down the street, I would constantly see pregnant women or women with children, it made me resent myself because I couldn't get pregnant. It had been two years, and still I had not yet fallen pregnant.

Early 2012, all our attempts to get pregnant had failed. I was feeling awful because I was convinced there was a problem. In the past, I had managed to get pregnant so easily and quickly without trying, but now I was struggling. In a way, though, it was a good thing. It meant I didn't have to carry a baby and then miscarry for doctors to investigate.

As soon as I could, I booked an appointment with my GP; Mike came with me for support. I walked up to the door and knocked.

"Come in," a friendly voice responded. I pushed open the door, and Dr. Ali warmly greeted me with a smile. She was a petite Asian woman, dressed in western clothing and a hijab. She sat at her desk as I entered.

Dr. Ali perused my notes and was very compassionate; she read what I had experienced and asked, "How are you coping?" She was concerned, and I could see she really wanted to help me. Dr. Ali referred me to a gynaecologist. She also warned me it might take a while for the appointment to come through as it was on the NHS, but I would be put on the waiting list. However, waiting didn't bother me too much; I was just happy that I would soon be able to see someone. I had seen Dr. Ali on several occasions, and she was one of the best GPs in my surgery, from my viewpoint.

When I received my letter at home for my appointment, I was overjoyed. I was booked to see Dr. Morgan at King George's Hospital. On the day of my consultation, Mike accompanied me. We parked in the multi-story car park. It was my first time at King George's. It was a new hospital and around thirty minutes from home. I felt very eager and positive. Upon entering the hospital, it reminded me of Waterloo train station: the entrance was chaotic, with people everywhere. There was a Costa coffee shop to my right, a self-service restaurant to my left. As we walked towards the information desk, an escalator and stairs were leading to the next level. Underneath were two shops, one selling handmade gifts and a WHSmiths. We made our way through the disorder to the information desk, where I asked where the location of the maternity outpatients ward. We were directed upstairs. There was a common reception area, glass-covered desks with several sections for reporting on arrival, plastic chairs neatly lined, and a television. After we checked in, we sat with some other people waiting to be called.

A young man holding a clipboard appeared and called a few of our names. We followed him to another waiting area, containing a smaller reception desk, a padded backless sofa up against a plain wall, and self-help leaflets displayed on a shelf. When the doctor came out, she was tall and skinny with mousey brown, shoulder-length hair and black-rimmed spectacles. I felt intimidated by her as she asked me to enter her room.

Dr. Morgan was very stone-faced and a tad conceited. I didn't feel that comfortable with her at the start; she tried to smile, but a twitch was all she could manage. Thankfully, my appointment was quick. The doctor had asked a nurse to take my height and weight.

When I returned to the room, he said, "You need to have a few blood tests before scheduling another appointment in two weeks for the results and to find out the next procedure."

I found it amazing just how quick the first appointment was; in fact, it felt as though they just wanted everyone in and out as quickly as possible.

When I returned two weeks later, I was a bit more apprehensive. I wasn't particularly looking forward to my appointment. To my surprise, Dr. Morgan was a lot more welcoming and pleasant, which helped me to relax. I assume during our first appointment, she was having a bad day. I attended this appointment alone. I had a feeling that there would be many appointments scheduled and Mike would need to miss them due to work. The doctor thought my blood test results were fine and asked me to lay down on the bed in her room; she needed to take a high vaginal swab test to check for infections. Undressed from the waist down, she inserted a clear plastic speculum into my vagina to help examine the area. Guided by a bright light shining through a lamp, she then inserted a sterile moist cotton swab into me to obtain the samples needed. I was redressing while Dr. Morgan was filling out some paperwork.

She advised me, "Mike will also need to go for some tests, and you will need to return for another procedure."

I didn't know that I would have to undergo so many tests and realised that I had been naive in thinking that once referred, I would have IVF straightaway.

One of the tests that I had to undergo was a hysterosalpingogram (HSG). This was to check my fallopian tubes; they needed to investigate to see if I had any blockages. I went to this test alone without Mike. Performing the examination was a male Egyptian gynaecologist. I was a bit shy and ashamed about getting undressed. I was escorted to a small changing room, where I had to change into a hospital gown. Once I was ready, I entered a large room – in the corner was a glass sectioned-off area with computers, and two nurses were standing inside it. As I lay on the table, the gynaecologist inserted a speculum and cleaned my cervix. Then he inserted a cannula into the cervix and filled my uterus with iodine. The image was displayed on a computer next to me, and the more the iodine was going around my tubes, the more painful it was getting. It was a cramping, stinging feeling.

For me, it was unpleasant, or maybe I was just sensitive. The gynaecologist tried speaking to me to keep my mind occupied, but the pain was quite intense. After the examination finished, I was filled with emotions; I remember just sitting in my car crying. I was feeling sorry for myself – why did I have to go through all this? Why couldn't I just fall pregnant? Why was this proving to be so much tougher than I had initially thought? Until then, I was fine with having all the tests, but I had felt like it was never-ending, and I would never get to the part where I could have IVF. I felt lousy.

What would I say to Mike if I were barren? Would I want him to leave me to find someone who could provide him with children?

I spoke to him and told him how I was feeling. Luckily, Mike was very understanding and supportive, which was a breath of fresh air after my last relationship.

Mike said, "Even if you can't conceive, we'll find an alternate route. I'm sticking by your side, no matter what happens. Don't give up. I know we're on the right track to getting what we both want".

This was comforting to hear, and exactly what I needed. Mike knew about Grayson and what had happened with my past miscarriage. He wanted us to only concentrate on the present and immediate future, and to forget the past. I loved that.

Towards the latter part of the year, the lease on my shop was due to end, and I decided not to renew and to close my company. It had been open for five years, and I saw little future left in it. Unfortunately, high street travel agencies could rarely compete against the internet. I was an ambitious person, though, and it felt amazing to have achieved something I wanted so much; it was one of my dreams to have my own business, and I knew the risks of being unsuccessful would be high, but I liked to take risks and to challenge myself. I had the determination to achieve my goals; I had wanted to do it no matter how difficult. I don't regret having tried; it helped mould me into the person I am today.

four

CHRISTMAS ENGAGEMENT

CHRISTMAS EVE, 2012, MIKE decided that he wanted to give me my present early. He had organised a treasure hunt around the flat, just like my father would have organised one every Christmas morning for my sister and myself when we were younger. The main idea of my father's game was to keep us occupied for long enough so we wouldn't wake them up early. Sometimes, we would get stuck on a question for ages, so we would watch TV until my parents woke up to help us. I loved the idea; I was excited to play the treasure hunt game, and Mike had put a lot of thought into the questions and planning it. I was impressed! It brought back so many memories of my childhood. I felt excited and eager to answer the questions and win the prize.

I was enjoying myself walking around the flat, trying to find the treasure; the last question's answer involved a Christmas tree decoration. I foolishly thought it was one of the chocolate snowmen hanging up.

"Yay," I shouted as I ate the chocolate. Mike shook his head and laughed at me. "No, look further up." He pointed to the top of the tree. "Higher." I really couldn't see anything; then, suddenly, at the very top, I saw a heart-shaped Links silver locket hanging on the Christmas tree. I knew that wasn't a decoration I had hung, and I wasn't sure why it was there. As I turned around to ask Mike where it had come from, he was down on one knee. He stayed kneeling and held my hand. He looked at me nervously, smiled and spoke about our lives and our future, once he had finished he then asked me to marry him.

I was teary and excited all at once. "Yes!" I answered. Finally, something to look forward to! We popped open a bottle of champagne and snuggled up on the sofa.

I had always imagined myself getting married on a beach, barefoot, a small, intimate wedding with our closest friends and relatives. We looked into long-haul destinations such as Antigua. However, my dad wasn't keen on the idea, mainly as he doesn't like flying far.

We looked at short-haul destinations, and we thought we had found the perfect place, not too far away at the Blue Palace hotel in Greece. It looked perfect. It was

December 28th, and we were planning on putting down a deposit. Neither of us wanted a long engagement, and we weren't fussed about having a big celebration. We had been together for four years, and we were saving for a house. Everything felt like it was coming together: soon, we would have the results regarding any potential issues stopping us from falling pregnant, and we were engaged.

Three days later, on the 31st December, Mike received a call; his mum was ill and had been taken to the hospital. She had been unwell for a while and had suffered a few complications. Mike, of course, was upset that his mum had been taken ill again. She had developed sepsis and was admitted to the hospital for a few days. Mike decided to bring our wedding forward to the first half of the year. I could understand why, so I was fine with that decision. Mike's mum suffers from lymphedema, a long-term uncomfortable condition where excess fluid collects in tissues and causes swelling. A blockage in the circulation system had caused it.

Mike and I had a discussion, and after further in-depth research into getting married abroad, we decided that it would be best if we got married in the UK instead. We viewed a venue in the countryside and booked for April 1st, 2013.

Our wedding venue was a former palace, a Georgian mansion set in acres of manicured grounds and parklands. We were so busy planning; the next few months flew by. Between fertility appointments and the wedding, I had little time to dwell on the fact I still had not fallen pregnant.

I spent the night before the wedding in a cottage near the venue with my bridesmaids and my friend Rhiana, whom I wanted as a bridesmaid, but she was unsure if she could fly over from the States for the wedding. Stef and Chantal were my main helpers in planning and organising the wedding. We had only three months, during which my sister (my maid of honour) organised two hen parties for me: one in Amsterdam and one in the UK. My matron of honour and best friend, Lala, flew over around a week before the wedding. Lala works as a dance choreographer in the Philippines, she helped Mike and I with a choreographed first dance.

On the morning of the wedding, it was bitterly cold, but the weather didn't bother me; after all, I was getting married! I was getting ready and having my makeup applied.

"Look out the window. It's snowing!" one of the girls said.

I love the snow, and this made my day perfect. I would never have expected it to snow in April, and for me, this was a blessing.

We had a few guests who had travelled from abroad to share our special day. It was an intimate affair with just sixty guests during the day, and in the evening, we invited an additional seventy-five friends. I was really overwhelmed on the day of the wedding; I couldn't believe how many people had flown over to come and celebrate our day with us. I felt so blessed that everyone had made such an effort.

The day itself was wonderful. The civil ceremony started at 3pm with a pianist, and the seats were dressed in navy organza bows, with small lanterns to the side of the aisle and white rose petals scattered on the floor. Every bridesmaid wore a simple, long dress of navy blue and matching heels with a small, diamante hair clip, their hair loosely tied up in buns. Each carried a small bouquet of white roses hidden amongst baby's breath and was accompanied by a groomsman dressed in a navy three-piece suit and burgundy tie.

As I entered the room, I was dressed in a long, ivory A-line dress with a sweetheart neckline, accessorised with a diamante belt, and a dropped necklace. My hair was styled in a half-beehive with a side-swept fringe and soft curls cascading down my back. The outfit was completed with a diamante headband and a long veil. My makeup was simple and natural, and I carried an alluring bouquet of innocent white roses wrapped in a navy-blue hand tie. My father walked me down the aisle to Johann Pachelbel's Canon in D major. It was a magical moment to see all my closest friends and family staring at me. I felt very calm and smiled when I saw Mike wipe a tear from his eye as he watched me.

During the wedding breakfast, we had the pianist playing background music and taking requests. My sister's boyfriend, Bobby, was the games master and invented a game for all the tables to participate in; everyone enjoyed themselves. It was a great icebreaker. After the speeches, the ushers performed a song they had composed, which was very entertaining.

Once the wedding breakfast was finished, we had a casino table, a live band, a DJ, and Lala changed outfits and performed as a belly dancer. There was an open bar, candy stand, and a delicious evening hog roast.

Our bridesmaids – Chantal, Lala, Rebecca, Stef and Theana – and ushers – James, Tim, Paul, Seymour, and Steve – were a big help on the big day and I couldn't thank them enough for all the effort each one of them made to help the day run so smoothly; we didn't have to worry about a thing.

For a month post-wedding, we had friends and family staying with us, and we toured some around the UK, while others travelled around Europe, using the UK as a base.

Once all the excitement had died down, in September, Mike and I flew to Bali for our honeymoon, it was a good choice. We enjoyed our time in Indonesia: the hotel was perfect, and the food was fresh and tasted amazing. We even took a hike up a volcano at 3am and fried an egg on top; the view was fantastic, and our heads were in the clouds. We plan to return in the future.

After we were married, we were constantly being questioned, "When are you going to have a baby?"

I was asked this often – I think mainly because of my age; I was thirty-two at the time, and in Filipino culture, this was quite mature to be having a baby. I understood that it was often the next step after marriage, but unfortunately, it doesn't always go according to plan.

Every time someone asked me, "Are you planning on having children?" it reminded me of how hard it was trying to conceive, and they unknowingly upset me. No one realised the sensitivity of the question, but, it was like a dagger to my heart every time.

After our wedding, I was having a bad time, I found that I had lost all interest and pleasure in life. Things I used to love doing became a struggle, like a daily battle I felt I was constantly losing. I didn't get the same happy feeling I used to when I did something I used to love. I was always trying to escape. I was regularly irritated and tearful. My mood was always low, and I could not figure out why, I began feeling tired all the time. It didn't matter if I got twelve hours of sleep; I would still feel tired and want to go back to bed.

I faked smiles. Even at the happy family events where everyone was laughing and smiling with joy, I felt sorrow and darkness. I would sit and force a smile, so I did not seem moody to everyone around me. I found it harder every day; I couldn't motivate myself, and often, I would avoid speaking to people so they wouldn't ask me anything. I was still struggling to become pregnant. I just felt like everything was piling on top and slowly suffocating me, and I could not enjoy life.

Dr Rhiana Roque was my close friend, a qualified psychiatrist in California. We had been speaking a fair bit. I explained to her how I was feeling and told her about what I had been going through. She advised that I should get treatment. She thought I might have depression; I was relieved I had taken the time to speak to her and took her advice.

I saw my GP, and she referred me to counselling. The first treatment I had was group sessions; I attended around six sessions. The idea was to encourage one another to share experiences and to learn to understand yourself better. We were a small group of ten, plus our therapist. Some sessions involved group therapy activities; this would be problem-solving, skill development, and trust-building exercises. We weren't forced to participate if we didn't want to. Personally, I didn't feel like it was for me. After the group session, I had some one-to-one sessions, which felt far more personal and I much preferred these to the group ones.

I only told a handful of people; I didn't want everyone knowing I was suffering from depression. I only told Mike, my sister, Stef, and my two friends, Lala and Rhiana. Rhiana was a great support; and her advice was very useful. Since we were close friends, I found it easy to open up to her when I was struggling.

Both Mike's family and mine knew that we were struggling to get pregnant, so they were not constantly asking us when we would have a baby. I kept my feelings close to my chest; I never wanted to talk about my struggles or problems unless it was on my terms. Talking didn't help me, it just upset me, and I knew many people going through similar situations felt the same way. It's almost like it was easier to open up to strangers and people I didn't know or someone who had also experienced the same thing rather than people who were close to me. I felt like I was alone, just me struggling with not having a baby. I knew there were other women like me, but the thought didn't bring me comfort; I still felt like I was alone in this battle.

I was still feeling low and I returned to the GP, who diagnosed me with depression and prescribed Citalopram. I administered them daily, along with attending my weekly counselling sessions. After two months, I felt slightly better, but my mood was often triggered– by seeing somebody pregnant or if something thoughtless was said – it would spark something in my mind, reminding me I couldn't get pregnant, and I would fall backwards again.

It was 2014, and my sister was visiting me at home. She was engaged and planning on getting married the following year, we were sat together in the living room having a chat about weddings.

She seemed slightly distracted, or on edge, then she said, "I have something to tell you – I'm pregnant!"

Her words brought the biggest smile to my face. I was initially happy for her; of course, I was. I knew that she would want to start a family straightaway, and I had a feeling she wouldn't have the same issues I did. I thought that having a niece or nephew would help take away from the urges of having a baby and would help overcome my depression. I was heartbroken at the same time, and I cried a lot. Hearing my family speak about her pregnancy frequently was like pouring alcohol on an open wound. I genuinely felt happy for the first time in ages, but to constantly hear about her pregnancy was difficult. Chantal had not been trying for too long to get pregnant, and I felt a bit jealous at the fact that she fell pregnant so easily, but I didn't dwell on it. I focused on the fact that we would have a new baby in the family soon.

five

HOW LONG?

I STARTED WORKING UP-TOWN for a company that specialised in business travel. When I started, I was originally based in Farringdon; I stayed there for around a month before asking, "Can I be transferred to a different team?" I didn't get along with my colleagues. My area manager agreed to my transfer, and I was reassigned not too far away in Clerkenwell.

I worked with Emma at this time; we had met each other through a mutual friend at a wedding a few years previously. When we first met, I wasn't too sure if we would get along, as I found her to be very boisterous, and she found me to be rude. We were not close friends;

we just knew each other enough to smile and wave 'hello' in passing. Emma and I were put on the same team, and she became my new assistant team leader; this meant that we would spend almost every day together and we got to know each other well. She helped me a lot when it came to adjusting to my new team; she turned out to be different from my initial judgment. The more time we spent together I realised how caring and thoughtful she was. I knew that I could call her a new friend.

On February 20th, 2015, my niece Sienna was born. It was a Friday, and I was highly-strung that day, as I wanted to meet her so badly. Work refused to give me time off to visit my sister at the hospital. My manager said, "Your sister isn't classified as your immediate family".

I was gutted when I was told this. It was only one day until the weekend, but it felt like the longest day. My sister and mum were constantly updating me with photos, and my whole family was together. I felt left out.

When I finally managed to visit my sister and niece they were still in hospital, I remember I turned up with a bunch of flowers which security confiscated from me, that didn't matter though as I was so excited. When I first laid eyes on Sienna she was wrapped up in a blanket with a little hat on, she was so tiny, such a small bundle of joy. I lifted her up and gave her a kiss on the cheek, my heart skipped a beat; Sienna was perfect in every way. I knew how much I yearned for a baby, but with the love I felt I also knew how much I wanted to protect and love my niece.

After a few months, when I realised the company I worked for wasn't for me, I started applying elsewhere. I quickly established that in corporate travel, it was steered more into using in-house computer systems rather than being qualified in travel. Corporate travel is aimed at businesses with employees travelling for the company. No matter how often they travel or the destination, the company pay for the expense. I preferred the leisure side of the industry, where it is aimed more towards personal service, building a rapport with clients, and actually selling them a holiday.

I found a new opening not too long after searching; it was at a luxury travel company based just thirty minutes away from home. I was happy to be able to drive to work, as I hated having to travel by tube. I was not too fond of the chaos on the commute into work, and on the way home, I wanted to relax. The tube was anything but relaxing.

In April, I started in my new role at the luxury travel company. I was much more content. I was glad I had tried business travel but realised swiftly it wasn't for me. I made the right choice moving back into leisure.

Our office was a tiny room painted plain white, and it featured a large window that faced a characterless rooftop. My desk had a computer, my folders, and a few bits of stationery; in front of me was a desk divider so I couldn't directly see the person sat opposite me. Above was an air conditioning unit, which constantly blasted out cold air, a few chests of drawers full of leaflets, and two empty desks.

Our team was really small. There were around six of us working in the luxury division of the company. I loved going to work every day. The company had a very laid-back atmosphere, and I was in control of my own bookings and clients. It felt as if I was running my own business, just without the added stress. I was feeling good about myself again and looking forward to the future.

Mike and I were still under the care of King George's Hospital; we were still having investigations and waiting to discover if there was a reason why we were struggling to conceive.

On June 11th, 2015, Dr. Morgan couldn't detect any problems or issues we had. She advised us that we would be eligible for IVF, and we would be registered on the NHS waiting list. We were delighted at the news. She then said that the waiting time would be at a minimum of nine months.

"How long? Nine months! Are you kidding me?" I could have a baby in that time.

I was pleased – of course, I was – but I was also gutted. I had already waited so long; why was the process so drawn out? I had assumed that the treatment would commence once the tests had ended. I was impatient and more than ready to get started. Having IVF privately was expensive. However, I was intrigued to find out the exact price and to explore the system. Would it take as long as the NHS? It had been tedious practice since the beginning, and the thought of having to wait another nine months was discouraging. Mike agreed that we should look into every possibility. I promptly started investigating.

First, I contacted a clinic two hours away based in Cambridge. Dr. Morgan had mentioned it. However, after discussing it with Mike, he rightly pointed, "If you need to attend as many appointments as you had beforehand, then the travelling would be too time-consuming."

I took his advice and scouted local options. I found The Valley, a private hospital not too far away. I contacted them and scheduled a consultation. It was much better suited to our needs.

For the first time in ages, I felt like we were finally on the path to getting some real answers. We had an appointment with Dr. Atalla on September 16th, 2015; I was nervous and not sure what to expect. Upon first meeting her, I found her to be a very stern lady and quite domineering. She was perceived as humourless and very serious-minded, but I liked that about her; because it felt like she wouldn't take any nonsense. She could crack the whip if needed and keep me in line. She was very informed, confident, and was clearly highly qualified.

During the consultation, I asked her, "What would the time frame be to start the process?" After all, this was what everything hinged on.

To my surprise, she told me, "You can start on your next menstrual cycle. I can use the previous blood tests you had drawn up at King George's. However, you would need to have additional bloods taken and a test to check your natural FSH (follicle-stimulating hormone) levels".

I was pleased when I heard this, it meant that I wouldn't have to retake all the tests again and waste more time. Mike would need to undergo another semen analysis to check his sperm count, and I was advised that I would have a 3D aqua scan performed.

A 3D aqua scan is also known as a hydro scan, or saline infusion sonography. It was used to show the outline of my womb. The scan took around thirty minutes to complete. During the aqua scan I wasn't given anaesthetic; the medical staff only advised to take painkillers for two hours before the procedure. The scan would show if I had any fertility issues such as fibroid, adhesions or endometrial polyps.

Just before I left my initial consultation, Dr. Atalla mentioned, "You may need to lose a few pounds. If you fail to do so by your next appointment, I won't be able to push through with the procedure."

I was taken aback by her suggestion that I should lose weight. I was already experiencing a lack in self-confidence, so it shocked me yet at the same time amused me; she was being brutally honest and this proved that she wasn't reluctant in getting the job done. It was the push that I needed.

She explained, "Everything will be based around your menstrual cycle, and the whole process will take a month for treatment to complete from start to finish."

This was, of course, far quicker than the estimated nine months wait time I was quoted by the NHS. The cost didn't seem as bad as we had expected and so, after weighing up the options, we dipped into our savings and pushed ahead with the private treatment. When it came to leaving time at The Valley after my consultation, I spoke to the nurses outside the room, Marion and Abi. Whilst we were chatting, I mentioned to them that Dr. Atalla had advised me that I needed to lose weight, or she would not proceed with the treatment. This didn't astonish the nurses.

"Yes, Dr. Atalla is very strict, and she has turned people down before, don't take it to heart. She is very good at her job; you will be in good hands."

This was what I needed to hear and was what propelled me onto the journey of losing weight. I had just less than one month to get to the target weight. Knowing I had to lose the weight for her to agree to treatment was my motivation.

At work, there was a new female manager that started – Vicky. We were getting on great. Our company was now building up the team. I tried to recruit and convince Emma to leave the other company and join me in luxury travel. She wasn't that keen at first, but after two months she did. At first, she didn't really enjoy the job as much as I did – she found it slow-paced and uninteresting, and she made a point of making this known!

I convinced her, "Hold out for longer. Once you have your own client base, it becomes overwhelmingly busy."

I had been working for the company for a year by now. However, the beginning was just as slow for me. But over time, I had built up my own portfolio. Emma ended up enjoying the job and is still at the company to this date.

The time rapidly approached for my aqua scan at The Valley Hospital. My sister and niece attended my appointment with me. This scan was to be performed in the fertility unit by Dr. Atalla – the aqua scan was an internal investigation. The procedure required the doctor to insert a catheter through my vagina into the womb; the balloon would then be inflated to keep the catheter in place. Then saline was then injected through the catheter. It was very uncomfortable and felt like a really bad period cramp. After the scan, I was prescribed antibiotic prophylaxis to prevent infection. Dr. Atalla would receive the results directly and let me know her findings and what the next step would be.

Dr. Atalla performed most of the investigations herself, including IVF procedures. I liked knowing she was with me all the time; it made the whole procedure more intimate. I wasn't just another patient; all the staff knew me on a first-name basis. During my follow-up consultation, I prayed that I had lost the weight needed.

I found out the results of my blood tests, Mike's results from his semen analysis, and the findings from my aqua scan. We also discussed options for treatment, the different drugs involved, risks and hazards, success rates, and multiple pregnancies.

After reviewing the test results, she advised, "The pelvic ultra-scan shows a normal-sized uterus, the endometrium is all well defined, and everything else is fine." I thought it was great news, but then she explained, "The natural killer cell test came back indicating high levels of absolute CD69 natural killer count." It did not make sense to me, so she had to clarify.

She explained, "The CD69 killer count could be a contributing factor to your recurrent miscarriages. I'm happy for you to proceed with IVF straightaway. If you decide to go ahead with it, you will need to undergo two sessions of intralipids to coat your CD69 killer cells."

Dr. Atalla started me on the intralipid infusion. This is a dietary supplement for people with immune disorders. Natural killer cells are an autoimmune disorder, which prevented an embryo from attaching to the lining of my uterus. My immune system attacked anything foreign entering my body. The intralipid infusion was a highly calorific mixture of natural fats containing egg yolk and soya oil, which was administered through an IV drip. The intralipids would downregulate the active killer cells to help increase my success in pregnancy. These were going to be injected into my bloodstream every four weeks.

I felt like we were finally getting somewhere; we were no longer searching for reasons. We finally had an answer to, "Why is this happening to me?" I had been sure there was something wrong with me, and it was a relief to discover that my intuition was correct. It was also a great relief to discover that many women still get pregnant and have healthy babies with the same issues as I was experiencing. It meant there was hope.

I had been working hard to lose the weight but, I was scared it might not be enough; thankfully, the doctor confirmed that it was and told me I had done well. At this appointment, Dr. Atalla was a lot friendlier, which in return made me feel a lot more at ease.

One of the main side effects of IVF is ovarian hyperstimulation syndrome (OHSS); this is caused by fertility medication used to stimulate the ovaries. The symptoms usually began three to five days after the hCG trigger injection, and some symptoms could be delayed, occurring up until seven days after the embryo transfer. If you are diagnosed with OHSS, you will suffer abdominal discomfort, bloating, nausea, weight gain, and mild abdominal swelling. Most women could alleviate mild symptoms by drinking lots of fluids and taking analgesia to assist with pain. If it more severe, you might need to be hospitalised, and it could cause blood clotting, kidney and liver impairment, or twisted ovaries. Even having been told all this, I still agreed; I wanted a baby no matter how painful getting pregnant would be or the risks involved.

I began the long protocol on day twenty-one of my cycle, this was on October 7th. First, I started with two weeks of nasal spray; to temporarily reduce the level of oestrogen in the body produced by the ovaries and to artificially stimulate ovulation. The nasal spray was to be absorbed into the bloodstream through the supply of blood vessels in the lining of the nose. The medicine is absorbed even if you have a cold.

Just after starting the private treatment, we were

thrown a curveball: a letter from NHS St Andrew's Hospital stating, you can attend an appointment to see a consultant. It mentioned that I could start IVF treatment in December. I was astounded, and so was Mike; we had been told that we would have to wait nine months, and it had been nowhere near that long yet. We had started paying for medical care at the private clinic, so we decided to carry on privately as we were already in mid-treatment.

"I'm not too worried. If we had chosen the NHS option, I am sure the treatment wouldn't have commenced that fast, I'm confident there would be another series of tests to delay starting. It's taken years to even get to this point," I said to Mike. We now had the option to take the NHS route. They had offered us three rounds; we attended the appointment so we wouldn't lose our space, but we would finish the course with Dr. Atalla first before taking up the NHS offer.

At St Andrew's hospital, we were advised, that they wanted to perform an ICSI (intracytoplasmic sperm injection) opposed to the other common fertility treatment IVF (In Vitro Fertilisation); they said that Mike's sperm count wasn't as strong as the previous tests and that fertility treatment would be more successful undergoing ICSI. This was a form of IVF, a technique in which a single sperm is injected into the centre of an egg. ICSI was the most common and successful treatment for male infertility. However, we had already started our IVF treatment at The Valley, and Dr. Atalla advised us that

Mike's semen was fine, so I was not sure how accurate St Andrew's tests were. The hospital never even tested for my natural killer cells, which led me to believe that the private route we chose was the better option. If not, I may not have known about my killer cells for many years. I found the whole approach at the NHS hospital less personal, particularly as we were told that group sessions would be needed. They wanted us to share our experience with others; we weren't particularly keen on this idea. We were fortunate enough to be able to make this decision, and appreciate that other couples might not have the same options. We declined the NHS offer and continued down the track we were already on.

Back at The Valley, my next step was a transvaginal scan. Mike accompanied me to the appointment, which was performed downstairs within the hospital. The sonographer took photographs of my ovaries to see if the nasal spray had worked. Once the photos were taken, she printed them off, and I walked around the fertility department to hand them to Dr. Atalla to analyse.

"The nasal spray worked!" Dr. Atalla told us, we were over the moon.

The next step of the process was injections; I had to inject into the muscle between my back and buttock every night with 225 Fostimon. This contained urofollitropin, a form of natural sex hormone called follicle-stimulating hormone (FSH). It was to help stimulate the production of eggs this had the same effects as natural FSH.

I was given the injections to administer at home.

Abi showed me how to inject myself, in case I wanted to and showed Mike where on my behind, he would have to inject me. Some women injected themselves, but personally, I wanted Mike to inject me, as it was something we were doing together, plus I wasn't flexible enough to reach the injection area.

I was prescribed the injections straightaway to take home, along with my yellow needle disposable box and a bag of two-needle types (blue and red) I would use the blue needle to draw up the medication into the syringe, and then the red needle would be the one inserted into the muscle above my buttock. The red needle needed to be thicker and longer, as the muscle was deeper than the subcutaneous layer of skin. Every night I would feel anxious around the time of the injections. I was not a fan of needles, and although all the blood tests had helped me to get used to them, this particular injection was extremely painful. The needle was thick and sharp, and I could feel the medicine as it entered my body. After the injection, I would have to rub it vigorously, as I would be left with a hard lump on my back that would then bruise, making the area tender and sore for the injection the following day. I tried a variety of numbing creams to help desensitise the area, but they didn't help. I then tried ice cubes; amazingly, they worked. This made the whole process a bit more bearable. Some days I would cry when having the injection, the physical pain had built up, as well as my hormones and emotions. Some nights I would have a photo of my niece in front of me for inspiration, the photo would help distract me from the pain and give me hope that one day I would have my own child.

Once the follicles were big enough, they would be ready for collection. I underwent more blood tests and scans to check that everything was working, as it should be. I attended a few of these appointments alone since they were always during the day when Mike was working. I didn't mind, though, as I could sit down in the waiting room with a cup of tea and chat with Marion, the front-desk receptionist. Every time I saw her at the hospital, she always made a point of finding out how I was getting along. She would ask how I was feeling, and I loved the selfless attention I received from her.

Thirty-seven hours before my egg collection, I had to administer a final trigger injection, to induce ovulation, and to help the eggs mature ready for the collection. I performed this injection myself into my tummy; it was an emotional moment, as I knew the egg collection would be the final stage before my transfer.

Six

THIS IS ALL I WANT

WE MADE OUR WAY to the Fertility Academy London based in Marylebone; Mike was with me holding my hand as we checked into a melancholy building that reminded me of the Fawlty Towers hotel. The clinic was based inside an old-fashioned apartment. We had our photos taken at check-in for ID cards; we then sat in the waiting area, which contained lots of individually concealed sections. The whole waiting room was dull and uninviting.

Once I was called in, the room was set out like a hospital ward with separated bed areas. I was handed a gown to change into, I then waited to be called into the operating room to be sedated. In the room it was Dr. Atalla who sedated me, she also performed my egg collection. She used a needle that passed through my vagina and into each ovary under ultrasound guidance. The procedure took around twenty minutes.

When I woke up, I was a bit sore, and I was lightly bleeding. Mike explained that I wasn't asleep long, and during the time I was under, he had been called to produce a fresh sperm sample, which would be used to inseminate the eggs later that day. Once my eggs had been collected, they were mixed with Mike's sperm in the laboratory; after sixteen to twenty hours, they're checked to see if any of the embryos fertilised. I was discharged after the collection procedure and started more daily injections.

This time, I needed to inject myself daily in the stomach with 40mg Clexane, a blood thinner; I also needed to rectally administer Cyclogest pessaries twice daily until my embryo transfer. In addition to this, I had daily doses of Folic acid, Pregnacare, and Prednisolone tablets until I would able to take a pregnancy test. It was a lot of medication to remember day-to-day.

I received a phone call the day after collection; they advised me that Dr. Atalla managed to collect ten eggs. However, after fertilisation one was too mature and died, leaving us with nine, which was still a high amount.

As my embryos were of good quality, we had the option to culture them into blastocysts or to just freeze them as they were. We decided to develop them into six-day blastocysts to increase the chances of pregnancy. If an embryo cannot reach the blastocyst stage, implantation and pregnancy cannot occur. All nine survived the fertilisation period and were of high grades. We were then faced with another question; we were asked how many eggs we wanted to transfer back into my uterus. It was a big decision to make; we decided on implanting one embryo since more than that would create a higher risk of multiples. The remainders of the blastocysts were frozen and, if needed, could be defrosted at a later date.

On the day we were called back to the Fertility Academy London, for the embryo transfer, we checked back into the Fawlty Towers. The embryo transfer day was an exciting and stressful milestone during my fertility treatment. After weeks of medications and monitoring, the egg retrieval procedure and the anxious waiting to see if the embryos had developed meant that the final step of the IVF process was full of potential. Once the embryos had been placed in the uterus, before becoming officially pregnant, there was one more step: implantation.

I was shown to a bed and handed a gown to change into. I needed to fill out some questionnaires and consent forms. I tried to feel calm, but I was antsy. It was explained that my bladder needed to be full to perform the treatment.

Mike could accompany me into the room where Dr. Atalla greeted us with a friendly smile. I laid down on a bed; above was a screen with a camera, where I was introduced to some embryologists via video, they asked for my details to double check they would be returning the correct eggs to the right person. I remembered as I lay on the bed that I was experiencing many mixed emotions; I had no idea what the outcome would be.

The embryologists then showed us the blastocyst in a dish; I watched as they sucked it into a tiny catheter ready to be transferred. The nurse in our room then handed Mike a photo of the blastocyst that they inserted into the catheter with the grading details. I lay there with my legs open, as Dr. Atalla inserted the fine transfer catheter to move the embryo through the vagina and cervix into my uterus; this procedure was simpler than the egg collection and more like a smear test.

She peered over. "I told you, you must drink a lot beforehand, so that your bladder is full. Otherwise, the screen becomes cloudy and blurred, making it harder for me to see clearly."

Dr. Atalla looked at me disappointed as she scolded me. Although I had just finished a one-litre bottle of water, that didn't seem to be enough.

Dr. Atalla finished the transfer and ordered me, to rest for twenty minutes," before returning to my bed outside.

Even though Dr. Atalla said my bladder was not full, I was dying to use the loo; I just wanted to relieve myself, but I knew I couldn't yet. I was concerned that if I went to the toilet, the eggs would fall out. I didn't want to risk it, even though I had been told it was impossible for that to happen and I had no reason to worry.

Once I had permission to move, I went to the lavatory, I then got dressed, and that was it. Everything was done that could be, and all I could do was wait two weeks for the blastocysts to implant.

In two weeks time, I could take a pregnancy test. It was the longest two weeks of my life, having no idea if the procedure had worked or not. I spent my time praying and waiting, praying, and waiting repeatedly. I analysed every twinge and cramp. Oh, and of course, I googled every possible topic: implantation bleeding, earliest signs of pregnancy, how soon do pregnancy tests work, and on and on. It was probably the worst thing I could do, but it was human nature. I hated having to wait. I was advised that I couldn't engage in any strenuous exercise, as I was at high risk. I needed to rest and lay down as much as possible. I could walk daily or participate in yoga or pilates. When I googled what the fourteen days would be like inside my body – this is what I discovered:

» Day one: the blastocyst begins to hatch out of its shell.
» Day two: the blastocyst continues to hatch out of its shell and begins to attach itself to the uterus.
» Day three/four: the blastocyst attaches deeper into the uterine lining, beginning implantation, and continues.
» Day five: implantation is complete; cells that will eventually become the placenta and foetus begins to develop.

- » Day six: human chorionic gonadotropin (hCG) will start to enter the bloodstream.
- » Day seven/eight: foetal development continues, and hCG continues to be secreted.
- » Day nine: levels of hCG will be high enough to detect a pregnancy.

Day ten arrived, and I could not wait any longer – I had to take a test. I didn't tell Mike I was taking it early; he would have disapproved. I was so impatient and liked to know things instantly.

"Positive!" I was overjoyed. After I found out the result, I couldn't contain myself. I had to tell Mike.

I still kept testing every other day until day fourteen, to be sure. As crazy as it sounded, even though the test showed I was pregnant, I couldn't believe it; I had the confirmation and felt reassured. Mike laughed when he found out and said I was a naughty temptress.

I called Abi on the fourteenth day to let her know that my pregnancy test result was positive. I didn't ring after day ten after I took the test; I knew they would tell me I should have waited and that I should call back.

After a few years, I was finally pregnant again. I had to return to The Valley the following day to have a blood test; this was to check my hCG levels. When I walked into the fertility department, I had a smile from cheek to cheek, and nothing could shift it. All the nurses congratulated me, and I felt so overjoyed. Daily I would look at my stomach, my hand resting on it, telling my baby, "Hold on." I wanted there to be a bump instantly so everyone could tell I was pregnant.

I treated the pregnancy as a new experience; I didn't want to regret the experience of feeling happiness if the pregnancy was viable.

The nurses were always extremely supportive and on hand. Without them, there the whole process would have been a lot harder. They observed the same situation all the time and were all very sympathetic.

Six weeks had passed, and the desire I was feeling was back. I wanted to start planning for our baby. Then, like previously, I started bleeding; it was a dark brown colour, and I was devastated. I read online that it could have come from implantation, but it didn't sit right with me. At the time, I was at home, and Mike was at work; I called him and said that I was going to go to the EPU at Whipps Cross for a scan. He left work early to join me. It may have seemed premature to others, but I didn't want to waste time – I had to know everything was okay.

By this point, I had attended enough ultrasounds to understand the contrasting facial expressions the nurses conveyed. This was why when I saw that all-too-familiar look on the sonographer's face, I gauged what was about to be declared, and my heart dropped – I knew I had lost the baby. The sonographer sat in silence, having no eye contact, inexpressive, just moving the scanner around, and pressing in certain areas.

During the sonogram, my heart was in my throat – I was apprehensive, I couldn't settle. The frustrating part was not being able to view the computer screen.

I glanced over at Mike, who was blankly watching the monitor. I wasn't sure if he knew what he was looking at. I tried catching his attention, but he was too fixated on the images. I just knew, though; I didn't need the words to be said out loud.

The ultrasound scan showed that the foetal movement had not developed; I felt sick, my lip quivered, I couldn't control it, and I burst into tears. I was developing a phobia for pregnancy scans – I couldn't bear to look at them; it was all just too painful. It was mid-December, and we were at the hospital, getting bad news once again. I was referred to a doctor following my scan, he read my notes and instantly said there was no viable pregnancy and that I would have to have another D&C operation.

The doctor also explained, "You will have to wait a little while before we can proceed due to the time of year."

I went home and waited for a letter in the post.

It was the festive season, but I wasn't in the mood to celebrate, although I had to make an effort, since it was my niece's first Christmas.

Everywhere I turned, there were pregnant women, babies, or parents walking around with strollers. I had grown to resent everyone; I needed to find someone to blame: medical staff, doctors, myself? It had to be somebody's fault – didn't it? At this time, my friends and relatives were also infuriating me with thoughtless and unintentionally hurtful comments. I wanted to be detached from everyone.

Mike and I were anticipating sharing good news over

Yuletide, but celebrations passed, and our joyful period was expectedly bleak. In the post, I received the letter for an emergency ERPC fast-track pathway (Evacuation of Retained Products of Conception) operation on December 29th. I had to fast from midnight. At 7am I had to report to the Plane Tree Centre. Mike came with me in the morning; I felt so unwell while waiting to be admitted – I was crouched over a ledge on the floor with a hot water bottle. I was bleeding heavily and suffering from lots of tummy pain, which felt like contractions.

Mike was calm; I could see him chatting to an elderly lady who was trying to find details for a cab office. The discomfort I was feeling started to get worse; it seemed like I had been waiting forever by the time I was finally called into the ward. I was in so much pain that I couldn't lift myself onto the bed; the nurse and Mike had to carry me. I was worried I had started to get an infection.

It turned out I was experiencing an incomplete miscarriage; the tissue related to the pregnancy had not shed from the uterus, and I was in urgent need of medical attention. I was instantly wheeled into the anaesthetic room. In the room, the anaesthetist was talking to me about Christmas as he injected me then almost instantly I drifted off to sleep.

When I woke up, the physical pain had disappeared. However, I was once again left with nothing but that empty feeling. The results from my operation showed the baby that I had been carrying was an abnormal male foetus, consistent with monosomy 21 (This can lead to birth defects, developmental delay and intellectual deficit) and trisomy of the short arm of chromosome 3. (This can result in distinctive facial appearance including a short head, widely spaced eyes, limb defects or structural heart malfunctions), I was discharged later that day with a seven-day supply of antibiotics. This included Doxycycline (antibiotics for infections caused by bacteria and other parasites) and Metronidazole (antibiotics to treat pelvic inflammatory disease). I was also prescribed some Paracetamol and Ibuprofen.

Two days later, on New Year's Eve, I went into the office. Work was quiet; most of my colleagues were still on their holiday break. I spoke to my male manager. Although he was sympathetic, he was more focused on me working and expressed how he thought it might be better for me to return to work to keep my mind off things. I didn't disagree with him. I just wished it were that simple; most people didn't understand that when you suffered from a miscarriage, it wasn't as easy as just 'getting over it.' Instead, you have emotions and hormones flying all over the place. Sitting at home was not helping, and I needed something to take my mind off it, so I decided I would work. Even if it distracted me a bit, I thought it would be helpful.

In hindsight, it was a poor choice; I should have taken time to let things sink in, to let myself grieve. I rushed back into work and didn't give myself the time I needed; this caused me to relapse into the black hole of depression. Mike wanted me to rest, but I was stubborn and insisted that work was what I needed. Mike suggested that I did what I felt was best for me. Truth be known, I didn't know what was best for me. In all honesty, I should have listened to him and taken that time to rest.

A few weeks later, a colleague from a different department entered our room; she was carrying her two-week-old baby. I couldn't help but smile. Maybe it was from the sadness of what could have been, or because I was broody and really wanted to be able to hold a baby in my arms.

"Do you mind if I hold the baby?" I asked her, and she turned around and simply replied no, tilting her head slightly.

"No. I don't want anyone holding her yet; she's too young."

I was taken aback but didn't blame her. I could understand; after all, it was her baby. Then, to my amazement, as she left the room, I witnessed her passing the baby to another colleague to hold.

My friend Charlotte was by my side observing. "That's just rude. She just said no to you and then handed her over to someone else? I suppose that is her best friend, but still."

I shrugged it off and told Charlotte that it was fine. I felt slightly humiliated. It had affected me more than I realised. I was so upset I went to the restroom, locked myself in a cubicle and cried.

After the operation, I had the urge to hold a baby; I was devastated that I couldn't. I just wanted to be a mother. The worst thought was that I might never be able to have children of my own.

Emma walked into the restroom; she saw me wiping away my tears and hugged me. She couldn't believe what had just happened; it had infuriated her. She knew I was suffering, and she knew everything I had gone through. People around me didn't notice the suffering I was experiencing. I masked it well, plus, they were too wrapped up in their lives to see the hurt on my face, only those who knew what I was going through understood and could see I was hurting.

After the incident, HR called me into their office to check I was okay; they had also seen what had happened and they knew of my circumstances. I was grateful for the chat and for the fact that they acknowledged what had occurred.

Emma was supportive, and at that time in my life, she was just what I needed – she was my rock. She was one of my best friends; she looked out for me and at work supported me on the days when I was struggling.

When everything returned back to normal at work, Vicky asked me to go for a coffee with her for a catch-up meeting. "How long will it take you to get over this? You have been so miserable."

Astonished by her question, I replied, "It's not something you can just get over." It wasn't as though I had been robbed and lost money, which could easily be replaced.

"What about previous times?" she asked.

"I don't know; the last few times it's taken around six months till I've started to feel better. Sorry, I'll try to liven up." It was all I could answer. I was peeved off that she had ambushed me. I knew that my mood could affect sales, but it was out of my control.

Carrying on with the conversation, she said, "You do realise that you can't avoid seeing pregnant people all the time?" Was she for real? She was so insensitive.

I wasn't in the mood for an argument, so I nodded and tried explaining, "I know. But, I can't give you a time frame for when I will feel better. Seeing babies and pregnant women is just difficult for me. I can't click my fingers and fix it."

Vicky and I were beginning to clash. I was under a lot of stress at work, and I felt like she was putting me in a difficult situation. I was struggling mentally with my IVF. I also felt like she had crossed a professional boundary by discussing my situation with other co-workers in the office. Which I didn't appreciate – I wanted my life with IVF to stay private, and I wanted to be the one to tell people that I chose. I only wanted to divulge what was necessary, but Vicky kept pressuring me for more information. In return, this caused a rift between us. I was usually quite happy to open up to people. However, this was a sensitive subject, and I felt as if she was disrespecting my privacy. Meanwhile, in her opinion, she was merely letting the other directors know my situation, so they were always informed.

Colleagues in different departments now knew my past, resulting in unwanted sympathy and attention.

There was just too much tension at work at this point, I didn't feel comfortable, and I wasn't enjoying it. I found it very hard to cope with everyday life; I just felt numb inside.

Luckily, Mike was by my side and was very supportive; he tried to comfort me in any way possible. I knew that he was also suffering, even though he didn't show it as I did. He was strong for both of us, and sometimes we forget how our other halves are feeling. He must have felt hopeless and frustrated; we were trying to do everything we could to have a child, and nothing was working – we didn't even have a real reason. I needed to remember that he was on this journey with me; even when he kept his feelings locked away to support me, he was trying to be the strong one for us both.

seven

FIGHTING THE BATTLE

TWO MONTHS AFTER MY miscarriage, I felt like something needed to move forward in our lives. Mike and I were not planning on moving to a new house, but we were always browsing Rightmove for inspiration.

One day I asked him, "How would we know what style of house we would like if we haven't viewed any?" I found it slightly infuriating, always browsing, and never doing anything about it. "Why don't we start the ball rolling by actually arranging a viewing?"

"That sounds good to me," Mike said with a smile.

I found a three-bedroom house available to view down in my parents' road. We liked the house and thought it would be a good first home. I called up the estate agents and booked a viewing. After seeing the house, we liked it – it was a perfect starter. We put in an offer.

However, the offer was turned down; the owners chose another couple that had children because they felt they would prefer the next owners to be a family. My dad ran the local neighbourhood watch and knew the homeowners. When he spoke to them, he discovered the reason for their decision.

Mike and I were outraged by how they made their decision. We didn't have children, but it certainly wasn't for want or trying! Positively, it meant Mike felt pushed to view more houses. We organised a day and viewed four houses. Last-minute, Mike found a house online that differed from the others we had booked to view. It was further out from the other properties. He wanted to add it to the list that day; I felt it was unlikely we could get a viewing on the same day. I called the agent, and, to my surprise, we got a viewing within the time frame we needed.

We didn't like the first four houses we saw; they were all too modern or too cramped. They just didn't feel right. When we first stepped into the house that Mike chose, a few other couples were viewing the property at the same time, as it was an open day. We walked into the first room, which had a log fire; the colour theme was dark grey, light blue-grey, and dark green. The art hanging on the wall had splashes of red. Originally, I had thought that from the way the house was designed that an elderly, retired couple owned it. A globe drinks cabinet was in the corner, and it featured wooden furniture. The room had a warm cottage feel to it.

We then walked up the stairs to the first bedroom, which had beautiful, white, wooden plantation shutters and a four-poster bed. The room was very spacious and was painted in white with hints of grey, fitted with white high-gloss wardrobes and a small fireplace. The carpet was also in grey. The decor reminded me of the Caribbean; it was very fresh and relaxing. The room felt airy and spacious; it was just perfect. There was a newly fitted contemporary en suite bathroom with a walk-in shower; the tiles were in different shades of brown and grey. Opposite the bedroom was a nursery: the walls were white with a set of elephant stickers attached to the wall; the room was minimal with a grey carpet and no beds.

The third bedroom was a guest bedroom painted white with a set of butterfly murals. From the prints on the wall, I guessed they shared my passion for travel. The bathroom upstairs was painted in black and white, with a bathtub and a small separate shower – on the wall above the bath was a decorative stylish rhino's head.

Mike and I looked at each other, this house was in a different league from the others we had viewed: it was perfect, and we hardly needed to do any work to it. It was modern yet traditional at the same time; it looked amazing.

At this point, Mike was now in his competitive mode. He said to me, "Keep a poker face so the other viewers can't tell we're interested".

We walked back downstairs to view the rest of the house. Just before entering the kitchen, we noticed a small cloakroom toilet. We went into the kitchen, which was decorated in grey with country-style cabinets, a beautiful black vintage cooker, and a granite bar separating the kitchen and open lounge. The walls were painted in duck egg blue, and a flat-screen TV was hanging from the wall, with an electric fireplace directly below it. The lounge opened up into a full glass secret haven; the conservatory looked like the perfect relaxing area and featured a sofa, wooden bench dining table, and wooden cupboards.

The house was perfect for us! That Saturday afternoon, Mike called the agent to make an offer; by 9am Monday, he was already chasing the agent as he didn't want to lose out on this house as we did with the previous property! We agreed on a price with the owners, and the sale was finalised within three months.

Between New Year and February, we celebrated my niece's first birthday and then her christening. I was asked to be her godmother, and I graciously accepted. On the day of the christening, I would decorate the room to be ready for the event. The actual baptism was at St Paul's church with a reception afterward in the Princess Suite at the Rosewood Hotel. It was a grand room; I was in charge of decorating the suite in a 'Twinkle, Twinkle, Little Star' theme. The colours that I chose were baby pink and gold. The walls were filled with foam golden glitter stars; the chairs had pink organza bows wrapped around the back of them. Each of the tables were decorated with a small lantern with multiple star cut-outs; these were attached to two pink balloons and one white, and around the centrepieces were diamond scatters and personalised chocolates.

For the entertainment, there was a candy bar and a baby sensory class with a small soft play area. Regarding food, we had a hot buffet spread. The christening was an elegant event.

We moved into our house on February 29th, 2016. There were some initial issues with the handover, which meant we didn't receive the keys to the property until 6pm. It was a very stressful day; Mike and I spent most of it sitting on the empty bedroom floor in the flat while all our furniture was packed up in the van, waiting to be moved. My parents came to view the property and helped us unpack and get settled in as soon as possible. We finished around ten that evening. The new house was just perfect for a family.

Despite being knackered, I found it difficult to sleep the first three nights due to the noise from the main road just outside the bedroom. In the flat, I was always used to silence, or a distant sound from a motorway, not the commotion of a road.

We discovered that the previous owners were a young couple with year-old twin boys. She was a physiotherapist, and he was a police officer – they were both pleasant, and I was in awe of them having twins. It was the perfect home; the only problem was it felt too big for just the two of us, and at times, it felt lonely. I imagined that one day, our lives would be blessed with young children running around. That was my ultimate dream. I knew that Mike and I were doing everything we could to accomplish that.

I had a follow-up consultation with Dr. Atalla; the once-stern woman had turned into a very caring and warm lady. During my consultation, she seemed disheartened by my IVF non-success.

She recommended, "You should postpone further treatment until you have seen a miscarriage specialist. Let me refer you to Dr. Hussain Shehata from the Centre for Reproductive Immunology and Pregnancy miscarriage clinic before proceeding with another round of IVF."

Dr. Shehata was a specialist in recurrent miscarriages. His clinic was based in Epsom, around a two-hour drive from us. I booked a consultation with him; however, the first available date was not until April. I was okay with that since it meant that we had time to get settled into our new house and get over the stress of moving. I found the determination from within to try for a baby once again, despite all our previous failures.

The first day we travelled to Epsom, I wasn't sure what to expect. In the past, I would have been excited. However, by this time, preceding experiences had taught me not to get my hopes up. I was, however, optimistic that finally, my issues could be pinpointed and solved.

Upon our arrival, we were welcomed into a beautiful, elegant townhouse, with wooden beam features. Stylishly designed, the waiting room was arranged with assorted coloured chairs; a dark leather sofa; magazines neatly arranged on a large, central, cherry wood table; and a top-of-the-range flat-screen TV hung on the wall. Underneath it was a large, wooden table providing raspberry-infused water from a vintage dispenser. Mike and I sat down; I felt instantly relaxed as I heard the symphony of classical music being played in the background.

Dr. Shehata greeted us; he had a face like someone you'd ask directions in the street: non-threatening and genuine. In his suit, he could have been a news anchor, clean-cut with a genuine smile. His movements were unhurried, choreographed and deliberate. When he spoke his voice was deep, and he conversed with the medical jargon I feared. Mostly, I understood what was going on, and periodically he would stop and smile at me before simplifying and continuing with details of the following stages. He suggested some more tests to be performed, as all our previous tests were now out of date. The results of which would determine the next steps.

The nurses tested me for thyroid function, which later came back high at 3.68. I had a full thrombophilia screen (to check if my blood had increased tendencies to form clots) that came back normal; a prolactin test (measured how much of a hormone called prolactin you had in your blood), which came back normal; a test to check different inflammatory reactions called TNF Alpha-TH1/TH2 cytokine ratio, which was high at 42.8; a test for Quantiferon TB gold (this blood test helped detects Mycobacterium tuberculosis, the bacteria which caused tuberculosis [TB]) – my result showed as negative. I had another test to check my natural killer cells count (also known as NK cells, K cells, and killer cells) – these cells played a big part in rejecting tumours and virally infected cells; my results were high at 209.1.

I had a lot more tests, which included thyroid antibodies (to check if I had any antibodies that caused the cells in my glands to work overtime), antinuclear antibodies (your immune system normally created antibodies to fight infections, an antinuclear antibody often attacked your body's own tissue – targeting each cell's nucleus), gliadin antibodies (this test was taken to help find out about celiac disease), liver function tests, and a clotting screen profile. Thankfully, all came back normal.

There were a lot of tests and results to understand. After Dr. Shehata explained the findings, he recommended his phase two treatment. Phase one included Humira injections one at a time, two weeks apart, followed by a repeat blood test for TNF alpha two weeks after the second injection.

He said, "I will need to see you again to share the result and to decide if you will need a further two injections or whether you can move on to phase two of the treatment. Around ninety per cent of patients respond within the first two injections, and ten per cent do not and may need another two injections".

I was hoping I was one of the ninety per cent because

I did not want to keep having more injections. Phase two would be the 'complex program.'

Due to results of a high TSH, Dr. Shehata recommended Thyroxine to bring the level below 2.5. I didn't have an underactive thyroid; this was mainly from a fertility viewpoint. I would need to stay on Thyroxine from this moment and throughout the pregnancy.

I was prescribed the Humira (Adalimumab), which is given if the TB Gold test is negative or if the Cytokines/TNF alpha is raised. The prescription was sent to my home in a cooler box. Once I received the injections, I self-administered one into my stomach (I also had the option of injecting myself in the thigh); the other injection was then stored in the fridge, ready for use in two weeks. Humira had been clinically beneficial in some patients with immune disorders associated with high tumour necrosis factor; Humira is a TNF blocker used for patients with elevated levels of TNF cytokines or NK cells.

Over the next few months, my depression kicked in acutely. No matter what Mike said to me, it was the wrong thing. I struggled to get through days. I did the best I could, but inside I was numb. Some people felt it was best to stay away from me or avoid the subject of babies altogether, however, the avoidance upset me more – with the right approach, I wouldn't mind discussing it; all I really wanted was support and people around me. I could not blame them, though, I disagreed with everyone, and I was being difficult. Friends and relatives were trying to stay positive by saying I would have a baby, but I found it hard to believe; it didn't feel like anything would work for me.

Family friends at gatherings would constantly ask, "When are you going to have a baby?" Especially since I was thirty-five and had been married for four years.

Couples able to conceive straightaway sometimes take it for granted. If only it were easy to change the perspective of one's mind. The speculation that people had was that we didn't want children, rather than thinking, "Maybe they are going through some complications."

Judgemental comments such as, "You're next," "Why don't you have any children yet, you don't like them?" or, "You need to hurry up, your sister is beating you," were all criticisms which offended me. I knew that wasn't the intention, so rather than snapping, I would just smile, walk away from the conversation in silence and ignore them.

The strain mentally was making life unbearable. I started locking myself in the bedroom, not wanting to speak to anyone, not even Mike. I was constantly irritated, crying all the time, and most of all, I felt alone. No one could help me. I felt helpless. I was falling back into that dark hole of depression. Only women who have experienced the loss of a baby through a miscarriage could truly understand what I was feeling.

The worst part of it all was feeling useless – like I had failed to do what women were essentially made to do.

The dark cloud descended upon me every time I lost a baby. Depression. It could only be compared with the death of a friend, and I could honestly say it was far worse. When a friend passes suddenly, we would view the body to say goodbye before they are to be buried or cremated; we have the company of others who are as grief-stricken as us. You can replay moments in your mind, a video stream of memories, which is a part of the way the brain processes the loss. You don't feel as alone because others are going through the same thing, and solace can be sought with other mourners. With every miscarriage, I was left battling through the euphemism to even recognise that I have been bereaved. What just happened? 'Pregnancy loss?' If there is no body, how can I grieve? I felt misunderstood, wallowing in a morass of grief over a person who has never lived. I almost welcomed the pain and blood that happened every time I miscarried, as these were tangible reasons to be upset. A miscarriage was an entirely private grief.

"How are you?" a friend would ask. I would wonder, Did they really want to know the blackness of my mood? Every time I lost a baby, I found it harder to comprehend. My intuition told me that for my friends, my situation had become repetitive and boring. More people seemed to be stepping away from me. With each miscarriage, I was crying out more for help, yet I felt less and less able to ask for it. I sensed that everyone around was seeing me as a burden, but I needed their support, I needed them to listen, even if it was just for comfort.

I was still working for the luxury travel company. I was

working long hours, burying my head in my workload, masking any feelings I was having. Despite my emotional state, I was making a success of my career, and I was nominated for Travel Agent of the Year. The awards night was held at the Lyceum Theatre in London followed by an after-party at the Savoy hotel. It was a formal black-tie event; Mike and my mum accompanied me for support. Unfortunately, I didn't win, but the evening was a nice experience; it helped lift my spirits. Long hours working was probably taking a toll on my body. I kept working as I felt like the rest of my life was empty. I had nothing else. I had Mike and my career – that was all I had to live for.

June 13th and Dr. Shehata had received the TNF Alpha result. It was now normal at 31.1.

He said, "I'm pleased with the outcome. I recommend the second phase of the treatment, which is the Complex NK cell treatment programme. This programme includes Prednisolone and intralipid infusions, in addition to Cylogest pessaries and Omeprazole. But there are possible side effects; in particular, the theoretical potential risk of cleft lip with the steroids to the unborn baby. Also, so you know, the drugs are not licensed for use during pregnancy, and there is a lack of scientific evidence from randomised controlled trials for the efficacy of these drugs for your condition."

He provided me with information leaflets, and I had to sign a consent form. We would take the risk – we would have taken all risks at this point to have a successful pregnancy. I had to continue with Thyroxine.

I could repeat tests locally with my GP and these results could be forwarded to him to monitor.

I was prescribed baby aspirin and prenatal multivitamins, which included Omega 3, Folic acid, and vitamin D3 eight weeks before I started the IVF process again. I was also under a lot of pressure at work. Trying to balance hospital appointments and my workload was proving difficult. Luckily, Vicky was being supportive in allowing me to attend my appointments, although that didn't stop me from feeling guilty for missing work – the overload increased my depression. I was travelling to Epsom regularly for check-ups, and intralipid infusion drips.

Mike came with me to an appointment where I had to have my intralipid infusion afterwards. He wasn't allowed into the room where the drips were being administered, so he took the train back to work, and from then on, I went to my infusion appointments alone. I would travel to Epsom, where the procedure would carry out with a cannula into a vein, either the arm or hand. Baseline observations were taken of my blood pressure, pulse, and temperature. Each infusion would take one to two hours while I was seated. I was able to eat and drink while the infusion was taking place. A member of the clinical team was present and monitoring me throughout the appointment.

Some patients could experience a rise in body temperature, headache, nausea, or flu-like symptoms; I was lucky not to suffer from any of these and could resume my normal activities straightaway. I didn't need to see the doctor, apart from when the nurses struggled to find my vein, which happened on several occasions. At one appointment, it took eight attempts to find my vein. A nurse, a doctor and then an anaesthetist attempted it. I've been told that my veins like to stay buried deep down below my skin. It left me feeling like a pincushion.

I had a set of two of my intralipids administered at The Valley, then after that, Dr. Shehata preferred them to be performed at his clinic. By then, I appreciated why Dr. Atalla wanted me to lose weight; it wasn't because I was overweight or to be vindictive, but more as a concern about how much extra weight I would gain during my treatment. I had two years' worth of intralipids and steroids. My body had been taken over; vanity was no longer an option.

I hadn't been able to return to the Philippines for a long time nor see friends or family living abroad, besides the few able to fly over for our wedding. I still had followers from back in the day and unfortunately these people would judge my photos on my social media accounts. I would receive comments on how much weight I had gained. The once-confident girl was now suffering from low self-esteem. It had affected me and added to my ongoing depression. I knew that I was gaining weight. I also knew that I would do whatever was necessary to have a baby.

eight

MY DARKEST HOUR

THE WEATHER FELT LIKE the start of summer, before the fiery heat of August. I could smell freshly cut grass and hear birds chirping in the distance. It was a fine spring morning, yet I was at an all-time low. Friends and relatives who knew what I was experiencing with my treatment would often tell me to pray.

"Pray for what?" God wasn't helping me. He was making me suffer.

I had been going to church on odd occasions during my medical care; it was a place where I felt comfort and calmness, somewhere I could think clearly and search for hope. A place where I believed if I spoke openly, someone would listen. Most of the time, I would just sit bent over with my face in my hands, crying. I didn't see how praying would help, and I felt I shouldn't have to pray to become pregnant. I shouldn't have been given this painful and challenging journey from God.

The heavy oak doors of the church broke open; I heard echoing around the empty church; I moved to a vacant bench and dropped to my knees. If I bow my head and fold my hands, God, will you hear my prayer? Are you able to feel my pain and inner torment? I began reciting the Lord's Prayer, hoping He was listening. I was so alone. Did I have the will and inner strength to carry on? I was usually a strong-willed person, but I was struggling to find the strength within myself. I was losing all hope and faith in God and the system.

I was very good at masking my emotions, so Dr. Atalla hadn't noticed my depression. Plus, I didn't want there to be a reason for her to stop my treatment – I had a feeling that if she felt I was mentally unstable, she would tell me to hold off for a while. We had spoken a couple of times about the difficulties of IVF. The treatment was one huge mental and emotional rollercoaster. I was very fortunate to have found a doctor and team that were very supportive. Even though I had the option to go to counselling, I chose not to. I made this decision after having previously tried it. Plus, I thought I could go through this treatment without help. I thought I could manage, and that counselling wouldn't offer me much support. I was stubborn. Dr. Atalla would ask me how I was feeling, and so would the other nurses. It was comforting knowing that even though I felt alone, lost and almost incapable, there was help around me, people who cared about how I felt.

All the emotional pain was leaving me with invisible scars that no one could see or understand. Initially, I was strong; I knew what I was getting into, but I didn't known that it would break me. Thankfully, Marion had seen it all before and knew what I needed to hear to keep me going and make me feel positive. She was like a fairy godmother, with no powers, just wise and caring words.

When someone suffers from depression, there is a big possibility that no one around them would notice, not until it is too late. When that darkness overpowered me, I needed to hold on to the light. The darkness was scary; it felt like I was getting dragged further and further into it, and the light was getting smaller and smaller every day.

Depression is the unseen, unheard silent killer. It is the pain that is too much to cope with, too hard to deal with, and so misunderstood.

If I killed myself now, how would I do it? Pills, crash my car, slit my wrists? What would be the easiest way? It can't be as painful as what I was feeling now. You can't escape depression; no matter how hard you try, it follows you like a black shadow eating away at you from the inside. It makes you feel like death would be less painful then living; it makes you feel isolated and alone, even if you know thousands are suffering like you. Depression does not just appear; it slowly creeps in and takes over every part of your mind and soul until you felt like you have no control over yourself.

I spoke to a couple of friends living abroad – even though they were far away. It helped; true friendship isn't about being there when it's convenient, it is about being there when it isn't. When you have a loyal friend, you can pick up where you last left off, and it was like nothing has changed. A friend that takes the time to listen to you makes all the difference. You don't always want opinions or advice, just to be heard by someone who cares. Often the friends who were not physically part of your day-to-day life – because they live so far away – were the ones to support you the most.

I was in contact with my friend, Grace. Grace had moved from Manila to Germany, then on to South Africa. When we first met, I was at the beginning of my career as a model. She was the president of the Professional Models Association of the Philippines (PMAP). I was taken under her wing, and she became one of my mentors. After moving away, we remained friends. We were speaking regularly, having moments where we would joke around and other, more serious, times where she would advise and comfort me. Grace repeatedly told me to keep my faith through everything and to continue praying. Faith – mine had floated away from me. She didn't take offence when I said, "I don't believe in God anymore."

She said, "I can understand how you felt, but please don't give up on your religion. You should go to church and pray the Novena over nine days." I did it for around three days.

One evening, I thought I would try Grace's advice again. I took out my rosary and prayer book. It was around 6 pm; it was dark, wet and miserable outside. I felt lost, so I got into my car and attempted to drive to the local church. I wasn't looking to sit in on a service, but to find solace, clear my thoughts, just sit there and pray. This evening, I drove to three churches and they all were closed. I couldn't believe it – I thought that churches were always open, ready to welcome their flock. I was bewildered – maybe this was another sign from God. I drove back home; Mike still wasn't home from work, so I went upstairs into the spare bedroom, crawled under the duvet, and stayed there all night.

I would often hear the opinion, "Depression is a sign of weakness".

I believe that people should be treated with compassion rather than being told their brains are defective, and that suicide is a cowardly and selfish act. You cannot know what demons a person is battling with internally. When that dark cloud arrives, life gets impossible.

Early mornings were no longer the pleasure they once were. One morning, my alarm woke me, I turned it off before diving back under the soft, warm duvet. I wanted to stay hidden away. I knew I had to get up and get ready for work; that was the only reason I forced myself out of bed. I stepped into the hot shower, and as the heat soaked my skin, I leant against the cool tiles, crying. My legs weakened, and I fell to the floor – should I do it? Should I take my own life?

I was completely broken, and I knew I needed help, I just didn't know how to get the help I needed. I stood up, turned off the shower, and picked up the phone to call Emma.

Both Emma and Mike knew that I was having these thoughts, but they didn't know the full extent. I told her about how I was feeling.

She said, "Don't go to work. Call the GP instead. Work might complain, but they'll just have to manage without you for a day".

It was true that I was under a lot of stress at work – I was working on a bespoke and complex booking for a hundred people, and I was the only person dealing with it. My work had always come first, but I had got myself into a situation where I was in over my head. It was time I listened, and Emma convinced me I needed to see someone. Something was eating me up from inside as if my conscience was telling me I wasn't good enough. Every day I'd plaster my face with make-up, wear loose clothes, and a fake smile, but some days, it was just numbness and emptiness.

I had gone from loving life and myself to hating everything and wanting a way out, any way I could find.

Someone once told me I was a strong woman; I thought at times that I was. I tried not to define myself from moments of weakness and fear but from the days when I found the strength to rise above it.

Thoughts played over in my head. My niece would never get to know me properly. Would she be told stories about her auntie? Could I let Mike find me lying lifeless in the shower and have him suffer alone?

Following Emma's advice, I took the day off and saw the GP. The moment I walked into the office, I broke down. As the doctor listened, it felt like someone, at last, understood how I was feeling; I knew that I would finally get the help I needed. The doctor was very placid the whole time; we spoke about the difficulties that I was experiencing with my whole IVF process, then she prescribed Citalopram once again. Even though I was at my all-time low, I didn't want to be on anti-depressants. I was worried that they might counteract the cocktail of drugs I was already taking every day.

I researched on Google to see if there was an alternative type of help. I came across the Miscarriage Association. After I finished some researching, I picked up the phone to speak to someone on their helpline. I didn't know what to expect, but I had nothing to lose. I had to try.

The lady I spoke to had a soft-spoken voice, calm and comforting. She asked, "What was your experience? And how are you feeling?"

I felt like I had a safe space to talk about my fears, and I was reassured that my feelings were normal. I started crying, and towards the end of the conversation, as I recognised what I was feeling, I decided I didn't want to suffer in silence anymore. I built up the courage to take the first step in seeking help. The lady I spoke to recommended that I join their online Facebook group chat to connect with other women also suffering from losses. I emailed a lady called Lisa and asked to be signed up; it was a closed group with authorised access.

Once I was a part of the group, I chatted with some ladies. It was great to speak to people who truly understood what I was going through. The reality kicked in, and I realised it wasn't just me, and I didn't have to feel guilty about the way I was feeling. I found myself helping others in the same situation as me, and knowing I was helping others helped me to build my inner strength. I wanted to use my experience as a positive and I was glad I was able to help others in their time of need as others had helped me. IVF is emotionally and mentally intense, also wracked with hormones.

I was pre-warned by Dr Attala that it would be difficult, but I didn't know the struggle would be so painstaking. I started swimming lengths every day to help clear my mind. I knew that if I wanted to try another round of IVF, I needed to build my mental and inner strength. I wanted to face my fear, make sure that I had gained the strength and courage, as well as the confidence to attempt it all over again.

nine

GIVING UP IS NOT AN OPTION

I T HAD BEEN FIVE months since my last miscarriage;
Mike was pushing me to try another round of IVF.

To which my response was, "It's easy for you to say,
but emotionally, mentally and physically, I don't think I
can cope with it anymore."

I understood – of course, I did – he would have
been going through his own battles, but it would not be
good for me to try again when I was already so unstable.
We spoke about how it was difficult to juggle work and
undergo treatment; I told Mike I wanted to try quitting
work before attempting another round. I thought stress
could be a high contributor.

I blamed all the stress on work. It was my own fault, though; I didn't know how or when to stop. I was so engrossed with working that I forgot to look after myself. As much as I loved working, I wanted to have a baby more. It was a big decision to make and left me thinking, What if I quit my job and still didn't get pregnant? What was I going to do while being at home; would I get bored? My mind would flutter back and forth at the idea.

Every day I had started to feel stronger emotionally and more like me again, but never the same as before, because losing a baby through a miscarriage changed you. I learned that pushing myself back into work so soon after the miscarriage was a mistake.

Towards the end of May 2016, I worked up the courage to hand in my notice. I was feeling a bit more positive. I remembered the morning perfectly; I was jittery and didn't know how I should approach my boss, Paul. I looked at Emma, sitting behind me. I told her I was going to hand my notice in. She wasn't as surprised as I thought she would be; in fact, she seemed more excited. She asked me when I was doing it, and I told her I had sent Paul an email and was waiting for him to respond. I had not told my other manager, Vicky. I respectfully approached Paul directly as he was the manager that recruited me and I felt more comfortable going straight to him.

Vicky soon came into the office and sat next to me she asked, "Are you okay? You seem a bit on edge."

Gritting my teeth, I smiled and replied, "Yeah, I'm okay. Thanks." Not long after I had emailed, Paul responded, saying we could have a chat at eleven as he had a couple of meetings first. I was fine with that, although I was nervous for the two hours while I waited.

Eleven o'clock came, and we went into a private room. I didn't know how to start a conversation, so I handed him an envelope with my letter of resignation inside. He looked at it. "I'm not going to open it, because I'm not going to accept it," was his response. I was taken aback by what he said; I didn't know what to say.

"What do you mean you won't accept it? You have to," I laughed, although the situation was not funny – it was more a nervous laugh.

He explained, "You're too valuable to the company to lose. Instead, I will offer you a proposition: a three-month sabbatical."

I considered it. That outcome seemed a lot more positive than I anticipated. In fact, I hadn't even pictured that proposal. I accepted his offer almost instantly and went back to my desk. I felt content, like a weight had been lifted off me. I could breathe and finally be free for the first time in ages.

I spoke to Emma and Mike; I explained what Paul offered, and they were both pleased for me. I was happier to try another round of IVF. I was due to leave work at the end of June, so that I could have three months stress-free, and if I still felt like I wanted to quit work after that, I could leave.

I had already booked to undergo another aqua scan with Dr. Atalla. I had an endometrial scratch booked in at the same time. This procedure was supposed to improve endometrial receptivity and help increase the probability of getting pregnant. I wasn't given an anaesthetic; it was performed with a thin catheter passed through the cervix, and then the doctor takes a biopsy of the lining of my uterus. I was scheduled to have a second round of IVF in July. I was also booked with Dr. Shehata, as he had a treatment plan for me.

"Come on, body; you can do this, let's try again," I kept telling myself, trying to stay positive.

During this round, Dr. Atalla proceeded with a frozen egg transfer; it was a lot faster than the fresh cycle as you bypass the two-week nasal spray and egg collection process. Both Dr. Atalla and Dr. Shehata prescribed me medication.

Dr. Shehata would perform my ultrasound scans, and then forward any relevant information on to Dr. Atalla for her to look through and analyse. I felt in good hands with them both; it was still very personal, and they made me feel at ease, for which I was grateful.

Around a week before the blastocyst transfer, I had to start my Heparin subcutaneous injections; these were to stop blood clots forming inside my blood vessels. I was prescribed Clexane. I had to inject these between 6–9 pm daily into my tummy. I was then scheduled for another intralipid infusion. My tummy was covered in bruises and was sore from all the injections I had been administering.

About three days before the transfer, I had to start taking Prednisolone (steroids) after breakfast daily until my pregnancy test. I also had to ingest Omeprazole daily with the steroids to help alleviate gastrointestinal disturbances.

Mike and I were already familiar with the whole IVF process. This IVF round was based on my natural menstrual cycle, and everything was carefully monitored. Once the frozen embryos had thawed and reached the stage of development needed, I was called back to The Fertility Academy London ready for the transfer. It was all starting to feel like a routine. On this occasion, we decided to return two embryos; we thought we would try to double our chances. Due to the previous experience, Dr. Atalla reiterated the high risk of multiples and not to take the pregnancy test early.

That dreaded two-week wait! I couldn't help myself; I was disobedient and impatient. I took the pregnancy test early on day ten; unsurprisingly, nothing was showing. I thought this meant that it hadn't worked as last time it was positive after ten days.

I felt disheartened; I chided myself: "Serves you right for not listening to the doctor!"

I felt awful. I convinced myself to wait a couple more days. Day twelve showed as a positive; I did a little dance in the toilet with a sigh of relief. "Yay, phew, a positive."

I didn't tell Mike I was taking the tests early, or he would reprimand me for jumping the gun, which I was. Despite that, two weeks was a long wait. I was climbing walls in anticipation. I spent lots of money purchasing different brands of pregnancy tests, as I kept convincing myself that if it was showing negative, and maybe the brand I was buying was too cheap. It didn't bother me that I was consuming so many tests; I just wanted a positive result.

Two days later, I was in high spirits; it was a nice, warm summer day, and I had the bi-folding doors in the conservatory open. I was enjoying not being at work. I was pottering around the house doing odd jobs when two butterflies flew in. I stared at the beauty of them; they looked so radiant and serene. I was talking to my babies in my tummy, describing how lovely the day was and how everything was going to plan.

Later on that day, I found that the two butterflies had died in the corner of the room: two elegant, yellow, lifeless butterflies. I couldn't stop crying; I was hormonal and as superstitious as I am, I took it as a sign.

When Mike returned home that day, he asked me, "Why do you look so unhappy?"

I told him the story about the butterflies, and I said to him, "This cycle isn't going to work."

He told me, "You're silly. The butterflies probably died because it was too hot."

Even so, I couldn't shake the gut feeling that something would go wrong. Two days later, I repeated my pregnancy test; it was still showing as positive. I called up the nurse, Abi. She scheduled an appointment for me to have a blood test.

When the results came back, it showed that I was indeed pregnant, but the numerical hCG reading was below the normal range for the number of weeks I was; the measurement was showing a measured level in milli-international units of 73. The nurse wanted me to retest again in two days to reassess the levels to determine if they were still rising. In early pregnancy, hCG levels usually doubled every two to three days, and to give an accurate indication, a series of hCG blood tests must be taken two days apart, and the readings compared. If the levels dropped, I going to experience yet another unfortunate miscarriage. Naturally, I was contemplating the outcome of the second blood test.

That weekend I was due to go to Champneys to celebrate Emma's birthday with our friend Charlotte. I didn't want to put a downer on the weekend; they were both aware of my situation and that I was expecting a phone call, but I tried not to bring up the topic.

Once we arrived at Champneys, there wasn't much phone signal. I felt restless and on edge, anticipating the results. Lunchtime was rapidly approaching, and after viewing the spa facilities, the girls and I decided to pop out to the supermarket, mainly so I could get a phone signal. While in the car park, my phone rang.

My heart was pounding; I stepped aside and answered the call: "Hi, Colette, we have the results back from your blood test, and unfortunately, the hCG levels have dropped to 62."

My heart sank instantly. "Oh, okay, thanks for letting me know, so what happens now?" As much as I had the premonition that this pregnancy would not be successful, it was still like a knife in the heart. I secretly hoped I was wrong, but regrettably, I wasn't.

"Your body should naturally miscarry within a week. Once the tissue has passed, give us a call, and we can schedule a consultation for you with Dr. Atalla, I'm so sorry this has happened again."

I called Mike and informed him of what I was advised. It was all very frustrating, but he told me, "Try not to mull over it for now. Just try and enjoy yourself."

I was eager to speak to Dr. Atalla again. I thought that all my complications would have been solved by now. I guess I was expecting a miracle.

At this point in my life, I was no longer shocked at disappointing news; it was what had become normal. This time I had suffered a chemical pregnancy, which is when you suffered a miscarriage before the fifth week of gestation. Low quality sperm or egg, abnormal hormone levels, or a problem with the embryo could have caused this, although low levels alone did not always cause concern. Ever since I saw those two butterflies, I just knew, yet the feeling of numbness hit me again. Devastation. Now, I needed to turn around, hold back the tears, be strong, and tell my friends I was going to miscarry. With that in mind, I should also try and enjoy the weekend.

I was a mixture of emotions – this was never-ending. I had persuaded myself that I hadn't been off from work long enough to be fully relaxed for the treatment.

I told Emma and Charlotte what had been discussed during the phone call. I could see they were upset for me; they knew what I had been going through. I tried to shrug it off and act like it didn't matter and carry on as normal. Deep down, I was troubled. That evening, I shared a room with Charlotte; she was having her own personal issues and also feeling down in the dumps, and we had a little chitchat about everything, then we both drifted off to sleep.

I had to stop all the medication prescribed by both doctors after I was given the news.

Five days later, I miscarried at home; I passed the remains of the pregnancy in the toilet. I knew once I had passed the foetus, it was small, and looked more like a large blood clot; I was so used to the sight already. I said my goodbyes and flushed the toilet.

Mike and I decided not to have a chromosome analysis investigation this time and put it down to bad luck.

ten

THE FINAL HURDLE

WHEN I RETURNED TO Dr. Atalla for my consultation, she had become more understanding and sympathetic to my situation. My eggs had been tested, and they were all highly graded. Dr. Atalla explained that my miscarriage in December was due to a chromosome being abnormal, and it was possible this could have been what happened again. She referred me back to Dr. Shehata for a follow-up and review. We needed to see what other underlying problems there could be stopping me from reaching full term in a pregnancy before trying again.

After my miscarriage, Mike and I travelled to Dubai with my mum, sister, and niece. From the UAE, my mum,

Mike and I flew onto Mauritius. I needed to chill out, I wanted to enjoy myself, and after all, I wasn't working, I was also desperately trying not to fall into that black hole again.

We were away for twelve days; the sun was blazing hot in Dubai, unfortunately not as hot in Mauritius. It rained a bit, but that didn't dampen the mood. We still enjoyed it. Being away gave me the space I needed to think and to get a perspective on everything. We managed to go snorkelling, explore the islands, and see some aquatic life. I enjoyed travelling with my mum: it was laid back, and we had fun. She was young at heart and usually open to explore or try anything.

Mike had repeatedly told me about his friend's wife, who went through IVF. They conceived a baby girl. Before her IVF treatment, she underwent acupuncture and changed her diet, and that seemed to work for her. For ages, I hated the thought of acupuncture – that must hurt – needles everywhere? But, it was one option I had not tried. Mike was constantly trying to research new ideas for me to try; after the last round, I took on board his suggestion. After all, what did I have to lose? When I built up the courage, I decided to call up a local Chinese herbal treatment centre and give acupuncture a go.

I attended my acupuncture appointment, and the Chinese doctor explained, "Most women have acupuncture six months before IVF treatment and up to twelve weeks into pregnancy."

I didn't have six months; I had two months, so we started there and then. I was called inside a small room.

The doctor told me. "Relax." She spoke little English, but we could converse with one another. She rubbed some alcohol on my skin to disinfect the area and inserted needles in my head, shoulders, and stomach. It wasn't painful, and after, she turned on a heater and left me for around twenty minutes. On her return, she took out the needles and gave me a little massage.

I would be returning to her weekly for the next five months. Depending on where I would be in my menstruation cycle, she inserted the needles into different places. After a month, I was more determined than ever. I had stopped working, so I didn't feel as stressed as previously, and I could now concentrate fully on getting pregnant. It was like a job, one I didn't get paid for, but the reward would be far better if it succeeded.

I saw Dr. Shehata for my follow-up consultation. He explained, "You are on the highest programme I offer. There wasn't anything wrong with your eggs that Dr. Attala or I could see. You need to remember that with IVF, nothing is guaranteed. You just need to keep trying."

Mike and I discussed with the doctors about starting another round of IVF; both doctors were confident that I had no issue, and this gave me slight hope. This was all extremely difficult for me to comprehend; I just had to accept that the failures were down to bad luck.

Round three. I hadn't been working, I started acupuncture, and Dr. Shehata added in a new drug into my daily dosage called Hydroxychloroquine. This was an anti-malaria drug used in the 1940s. (It had recently found a place treating conditions such as rheumatoid arthritis and lupus. This was because it has immune properties and seems to calm down inflammation.) I was to administer this orally six weeks prior to IVF, and until sixteen weeks of being pregnant. Prior to taking this medication, I had to have a full blood count, liver and kidney function tests, and visual acuity; my tests would be repeated every six months with my GP, and results would be sent to Dr. Shehata's office. The drug had possible side effects of gastrointestinal disturbances, headaches and skin reactions, visual changes, hair loss and pigmentation to the skin, nails, and mucous membranes. To me, though, all that was worth it if I could have a baby.

I was also re-prescribed my other medication Omeprazole and Prednisolone. I had to ensure that I was taking all the medications at different times to eliminate any side effects. I now realised how expensive all the medication was. We had to pay for all of it as we chose the private route. I needed a constant flow of medication, so I took my chances, and I booked an appointment with my GP to see if I could be prescribed any medicine on the NHS.

I was very fortunate to have a cooperative GP willing to assist me. She read through my notes and took me under her wing; she prescribed as much as she could on the NHS for me and put me on a repeat prescription. To help save more money, I also purchased a prepayment certificate. Just by speaking to my GP, I saved just over £1,800. Financially it was a big benefit, which in return boosted morale.

I was interchanging at Waterloo station via the Underground on my return from my appointment with Dr. Shehata when I crossed paths with a smiley, freckled-faced, ginger-haired dear school friend of mine called Joe. We had known each other since nursery and were close friends during high school; as we grew older, our lives separated. We hadn't seen each other that often since leaving school, just the odd occasions in the local pub or down the street. As rude as it sounded, I was planning on ignoring him and walking past. I think the feeling was mutual. I presumed he would ask me if I had any children, which I wasn't in the mood for.

We both looked back at each other after passing on the travellator; we then both stopped. Now, it was embarrassing not to greet each other. I walked back to him.

We kissed each other on the cheek, and I asked, "How are you?"

He was dressed in workman's gear; he was filthy and mentioned, "I just finished work. How are you? Do you still have your travel agency?"

"No," I said, and we kept talking for a bit.

It was a light-hearted brief chat, and after, we parted ways. I felt relieved that I had stopped to have a conversation with him. It confirmed I was over-anxious and sensitive. My spirits felt lifted; I think it was due to my having assumed the worst and being wrong. I needed to stop avoiding talking to people through fear of them asking me if I had children.

At home, based on superstition, I purchased an evil eye charm to hang up outside the house; I wanted to eliminate as much bad luck as I possibly could. As bizarre as it sounds, I would have given anything a try. It would either help or not, and it wouldn't hurt anyone by having it hung up.

Moving forward from adversity, Mike and I were planning a third round of IVF. This time we decided not to tell anyone we were going through the process.

One afternoon my sister came around to the house to visit. "I have something to tell you." Her face was lowered like she was slightly embarrassed.

I could tell by her facial reaction what she was about to tell me, and resentfully I responded with, "You're pregnant again?"

She nodded in acknowledgement. It must have been awkward for her to tell me, and selfishly I didn't want to know. Yes, I was envious, and yes, it upset me. I tried to restrain my emotions at the same time by bottling it up. I didn't want to get depressed again. I was happy for her, I really was, but I just couldn't discuss it with her, I found it extremely challenging. It was upsetting, and it was hard to hear all my relatives' non-stop chatting about it. I felt like everyone was moving forward with their lives, while I was stuck at this roadblock, still fighting to get over the barrier.

In a room full of people, I felt alone. The only people I could share my true feelings with were Mike, Emma, and strangers going through the same experience as me on the Miscarriage Association Facebook chat. I wasn't me, and I questioned myself, Would I ever be myself again?

When Chantal was sixteen weeks, she was planning on having a gender scan to find out the sex of the baby.

It's a very challenging situation to be in. I love my sister dearly and couldn't have been any happier for her. We tried to discuss the situation.

I tried to explain, "I feel uncomfortable seeing a scan photo."

She said, "I feel like I'm always walking on eggshells around you, and we have to suppress our happiness because of you."

I felt bad that she felt like this, but there wasn't much I could do about it. We were both just protecting our own interests.

After that, we were distant from each other for a little while. It was probably for the best: she was hormonal from being pregnant, and I was emotional from everything. When feeling low and vulnerable, insensitive words and reactions can hurt you – although I would never show it, I dismissed the whole topic and withheld my feelings. I was focusing on building the strength to have another IVF round; I couldn't allow myself to get too affected by the situation.

During October, Baby Loss Awareness Week was held; it is a time when you can mark the lives of babies lost in pregnancy or soon after birth. Parents mark the week either by wearing a pink and blue ribbon pin badge, lighting candles, or attending events. On the final day of the week, there is a wave of light where people around the world light a candle or candles at 7pm local time in memory of the baby or babies they have lost. I participated, as it helped me with my healing process.

Mid-October I received a phone call from my friend Carly. I had learnt that Joe had taken his own life. I was devastated. Replaying the last moments in my head, I nearly avoided stopping to talk to him; I was so glad I didn't. I looked back, trying to see if there were signs I could have picked up on to realise that he was depressed. Never in my wildest imagination did I think that would be the last time we would cross paths. Suddenly, I realised I wouldn't see him again or hear his voice. Could I have said something to him to prevent it? I felt helpless and confused. I felt even worse when I learned that he was suffering from depression. I knew that feeling all too well, knowing he had suffered falling into that black hole and that he could not be helped. I understood that once he had decided to take his own life, he would have gone to great lengths to conceal his distress from those closest to him because it was most likely that they would interrupt his plans.

November came around, and it was time to transfer some of my frozen eggs. Mike and I kept this round between us. We didn't want the confrontation of telling people if it didn't work. I had encountered other couples that felt the same way they kept quiet, fearing insensitive comments or constant questions about results. That was certainly the case for us. I didn't want to hear the constant well-wishing. I knew that no harm was intended, but it felt like salt being poured onto a wound.

Mike and I implanted two eggs this round as the last two failed. Dr. Atalla didn't question our decision – she had been with us every step of the way and was happy to proceed.

During the two-week wait, I remained patient and held out till the thirteenth day to take my test – I was getting better at being patient! The test was once again positive. I promised myself that I would always treat each pregnancy as if it were my first because I didn't want to miss out on any happiness or experiences.

I called up nurse Abi, ready to take my hCG blood test to check the levels. Each stage for me would be a stepping-stone.

Abi was absent from work when the results came through; I spoke to another nurse, Kellie.

"Hi, Kellie, how are the levels? Are they high?" I eagerly asked.

I could hear the joy in her voice as she replied, "Hi. You will be pleased to know they are high, very high."

I replied, "Oh, good, so better than last time?"

She laughed and said, "They are around 1200 mlU/ ml. It looks like you could be having twins!"

I was in great disbelief. I said to myself – Right, don't get too excited, but I couldn't help it. On cloud nine, I called Mike to tell him what the nurse had said; he was very apprehensive. He didn't want me to get too excited because he didn't want to see me get upset again.

Around a week later, I attended Joe's funeral. I sat separate from my friends as I was deeply mournful and felt I needed to be alone. There were a lot of people that attended the funeral, a lot of my old school friends, and people I knew from growing up in the local area. I was around six weeks pregnant at the time of the funeral. At the end of the service, I walked up to his coffin, paid my respects, and as crazy as it sounds, I whispered to the casket, "Joe, can you hear me? If you could help me in any way to fulfil this pregnancy, I would be grateful, and please, could you look after my angels already in heaven?" I was searching for any type of help.

While at the gathering after the service, two old school mates came up to me and asked, "Are you planning on having children?"

I gave my usual answer: "Yeah, sometime soon." I didn't want to tell anyone that I was pregnant and tempt fate, so I just kept quiet.

When I reached seven weeks, I started spotting again. No, no, no this can't be happening again. I rubbed my tummy every day. "Come on, hold on tight, you guys are strong, you are little warriors".

The blood was a dark brown colour, and even though I had been through this a few times and googled it a million times, I wanted to go down to the EPU to be certain. I spoke to Mike and told him my plan. By now, I was so used to going to these appointments, and somehow, I preferred to hear bad news alone. It was 4pm. I sat in the car park of Whipps Cross Hospital and called up Kellie; we discussed what had occurred and I told her I was waiting for my appointment at EPU. I had driven to A&E and was given a time slot of 5pm. Kellie spoke to Dr. Atalla and said that the doctor thought it was a good idea to have the scan. I was extremely anxious; I didn't think that I had lost the babies as I was still experiencing strong symptoms. I wanted to be assured; the only way I knew I could be was to have an ultrasound scan. Five o'clock came around quickly, my name was called, I took a deep breath, and the nurse assessed my file.

She asked, "Why have you come here today?"

I explained, "I had IVF, and I've started spotting." I continued, "Due to my history, I want to have it checked out."

She advised me, "I might not see a foetal heartbeat since you're still early."

I kept that positivity close to my chest. The curtains were closed, and the lights turned off as she performed an internal transvaginal scan. The dreaded computer monitor was to the side of me; the room was silent, and all I could hear was the ticking of the wall clock.

The sonographer instantly turned to me and said, "Everything is fine. I can see the heartbeat."

Astounded, I replied, "What? Are you sure?" Did I hear her correctly? I tried pushing my luck and asked, "Is there only one heartbeat?"

Surprised and smiling, she then asked, "Did you put two eggs in?"

I replied, "Yes."

After a couple of seconds, she replied, "Oh yeah, there it is, he's hiding in the corner, he is fine too!"

I felt the tears running down my face. I didn't want to get too excited, but the sense of relief was overwhelming. I had waited years for this moment. I needed to pinch myself.

"Oh, my goodness, I'm going to have twins!" I knew it was early days yet, but the smile across my face was massive. This was my biggest milestone to date.

When my scan was over, I couldn't wait to call Mike to tell him the good news. I was out of breath, trying to rush all the information out at once.

All I kept hearing him say was, "No way, really? We're going to have twins?"

I was so happy and excited. Mike was in disbelief for ages.

I had two additional scans at eight and ten weeks for clarification that everything was going well. We waited until we reached ten weeks before we told our families the news. Mike and I went to my parents' house at the beginning of December, and we showed them the scans. They didn't realise that there were two babies – they congratulated us and then we pointed out that there were actually two of them. I think they were also shocked; my mum was asking me lots of questions. She wanted clarification that everything was okay; she was slightly cautious just in case I miscarried, which of course, was a high possibility. However, I wasn't entertaining that thought or filling my mind with negativity, because I wanted to carry on riding the cloud I was on. My dad said that all the waiting had paid off by having two at once. He was right. It had paid off. When I told my sister, she said she already had her suspicions and was delighted.

We told Mike's parents on Christmas day; we had wrapped up a couple of hats and mitts. When we gave his mum the first set, she was crying with tears of joy; once she calmed down, we gave her a second set to unwrap. She seemed confused once she opened it – she looked at me and said, "No, don't tell me it's two?" We nodded in agreement, and she was shaking with happiness. She needed a glass of sherry, followed by a gin and tonic, and it was the funniest yet nicest happiest reaction I had seen.

By the time I had reached eleven weeks, I had a meeting with work. They wanted to find out when I would be returning; my three-month sabbatical had now turned into seven months. The company was going out of their way to kindly open a part-time position for me. They had deferred our meeting twice and were finally able to meet in January; by this time, I was already sure that I was pregnant.

The first thing the new HR lady impertinently asked me was, "Are you pregnant?"

Taken aback, I replied, "Excuse me? Can we speak about the job offer, please? That doesn't have any relevance for the moment."

The way she had asked me felt like the job was only on offer, depending on my situation. I found it to be disrespectful and tactless. By the end of the conversation, I had great satisfaction in refusing her offer, not because I didn't like the position but more because I was offended by the way she spoke to me.

After the meeting, I confirmed to her, I'm eleven weeks pregnant with twins and that I think it would be in my best interest not to return at this time, as I didn't want to risk getting stressed and miscarrying again."

Suddenly, she had a change of temperament and became copacetic; we finished the meeting on good terms.

eleven

A WISH COMES TRUE

I CONTINUED WITH MY acupuncture and ongoing treatment plan. This included scans, which I had scheduled with Dr. Shehata every fortnight. In between these dates, I also paid to have ultrasounds performed locally at a medical diagnostic imaging center. I needed to see my babies regularly to ensure they were developing normally and because it gave me peace of mind, due to being a high-risk pregnancy.

Dr. Shehata frequently monitored my blood, and I continued to receive my intralipid infusion therapy until sixteen weeks gestation. At this stage, I was advised to stop taking Progesterone and Hydroxychloroquine. I was then discharged from Dr. Shehata's care and into the NHS system.

During the initial stages of my pregnancy, I experienced early symptoms such as morning sickness and nausea. Luckily, the steroids I was prescribed masked a lot of my symptoms. However, my sickness was still palpable.

The sonographer at Whipps Cross was exceptionally good at her job; during my twelve-week scan, she asked if we wanted to know the gender of the babies. Personally, I didn't have a preference, just as long as they were healthy and that they would survive. Mike was more intrigued to find out; he wanted to be prepared for the outcome. In normal practice, at twelve weeks, it would be too early to tell the sex of a baby. However, the sonographer was confident that we were to expect a boy and a girl. Throughout the first and second trimester, Mike and I carried on paying privately for gender scans, and during each appointment, our sonographer confirmed that it was indeed a boy and a girl that I was carrying. We were over the moon; it could not have been any more perfect, our ultimate dream team! I wanted to go shopping straight away, but I also didn't want to tempt fate.

At twenty weeks gestation, I had an anomaly scan; a sonographer performed this. This scan was to examine the baby's development and structure, check the baby's growth, and assess the normality of the amniotic fluid and placenta. All my results came back positive. We were thrilled to pass another key milestone.

At twenty-four weeks, I had my oral glucose-screening test, often called OGTT. I needed to be checked for gestational diabetes, which is when high blood sugar develops during pregnancy. It occurs when your body cannot produce enough insulin – a hormone that helps to control sugar levels. I was apprehensive of this test, not because I was at high risk due to carrying twins, but because I was adamantly convinced I would have developed diabetes, as my father is diabetic, and both sets of my grandparents were.

The OGTT test took two hours, which involved having my blood sample drawn, followed by ingesting a whole bottle of Lucozade in the presence of a nurse. After resting for two hours, another blood sample was taken; this was to determine how quickly glucose had cleared from my blood. I was fortunate not to suffer from diabetes or any major problems that could develop during pregnancy.

My first antenatal appointment with my hospital consultant wasn't until twenty-six weeks in. I had contacted the hospital, questioning them why I hadn't been scheduled an appointment by any of the medical team. It turned out that they had forgotten to put me on the list. This delay was clearly a big administrative oversight, which could have had big implications on my high-risk pregnancy. I learned from that moment that I needed to have active participation and ask a lot of questions during my anti-natal programme.

Upon my first visit, I was asked a few routine questions. I had to provide a urine sample and have my blood pressure and weight taken. During the appointment, the consultant reviewed my notes, handed me a few forms to fill in, and booked me in for a follow-up appointment at thirty-four weeks to discuss my birthing plan.

During my third and final trimester, I was becoming extremely tired while performing the most basic daily tasks. My body was incredibly achy, and my lower back was straining under the constant pressure. I had to take tablets for my joints as the weight of my bump was taking a toll on me. I needed rest and relaxation.

Mike and I started to see the beginning of the finishing line, so this felt like a good time to take a final holiday (babymoon) together as a couple, as we knew that travelling would be a completely different challenge during the early years of parenthood. We decided to go to Abu Dhabi at twenty-seven weeks. We knew we would be guaranteed to have hot weather (the hotel and facilities were perfect), and we could do some last minute shopping for our babies in their wonderful malls.

The holiday was just what we were looking for, but as the week went on, I was developing more symptoms, especially suffering severe heartburn, to the point where it would wake me up during the night. I didn't feel comfortable; during the day, I tried lying on a sun lounger, but I was feeling abnormally hot because of the hormone change. I felt like I was overheating all the time. I didn't want to dehydrate, so I made sure I was consuming a lot of water. I spent most of my time under the shade or in the pool. I panicked if I didn't feel the babies move. I was overthinking the whole situation, and every thirty minutes, I would say to Mike, "Could they have overheated? I haven't felt them kick."

He would tell me, "Stop getting into a frenzy, go and cool down."

I would walk over to the pool, lower myself in, and as I cooled down, I would start to feel them move again. I think they enjoyed the water.

After we returned from our holiday abroad, I booked a photographer to take professional maternity photos. We wanted to celebrate our pregnancy. I loved my bump and being pregnant held such precious memories for us, a reminder of what we never thought we would be able to enjoy. We wanted to be able to capture this occasion and cherish it forever.

During the last bank holiday in May, Emma and Charlotte threw me a baby shower. I was very hesitant about having one, as I was unsure about celebrating publicly too soon and, I also I didn't want to risk upsetting anyone around me that might be having their own issues conceiving, I knew too well how this felt.

It was a beautiful hot day; the girls had hired a private singer and decorated the entire house for my shower. I could see that they had put in a lot of effort for me. I was overwhelmed by this kind gesture. The day felt surreal. I wanted someone to pinch me.

I thought, am I really at my own baby shower? Did they organise this all for me? Just like my wedding day, there was a lot to absorb; but unquestionably, I enjoyed the day and was filled with gratitude.

Carrying the twins became difficult towards the end of my term, as they grew heavier. The summer of 2017 was hot and humid. The glass conservatory was like a sauna. Insects were coming inside to escape the heat but were dropping to the floor. My hormones were in overdrive; I was trying everything to cool down. In the end, I bought a twelve-foot paddling pool, and wallowed in the cool water most days, just like an animal bathing in the Serengeti! It was refreshing and really helped to lower my body temperature. Even so, I still wasn't dealing with the heat. I tried other tricks, such as a tray of ice in front of the electric fan. It worked for a little while but was not sustainable. Sometimes I even sat in the car just to cool down and use the air conditioning. This led me to finally purchasing a mobile air-conditioning unit, which was about as good as I could hope for.

At thirty-two weeks, I was carrying a floor-standing electric fan down the stairs at home and fell down a couple of steps. This was because I couldn't see my feet – luckily, I saved my fall and landed on my hands and knees. Distressed by what happened, Mike and I went straight to Whipps Cross to have a check-up. It wasn't a hard fall, but I needed a clear conscience. The hospital was hot and stuffy that day; they had two electric fans covering the ward but no air-conditioning. The nurse walked over to me, analysed my notes, and performed a blood test, as well as another prenatal test called a 'non-stress test.' I lay down on the bed, and four belts (two per baby) were wrapped around my belly: one was to monitor the babies' heart rates and the other to measure contractions. I was handed a clicker and every time I felt them kick, I needed to press the button; this was to show how the babies' heartbeat changed while moving. This test would also show their oxygen supply. Overall, it should have taken about twenty minutes to perform. However, the test took over an hour because the babies were very active. At one point, the nurses asked me to go for a walk and eat something so that the babes would become sleepy.

During one of my routine sonographs, they saw that one baby (A) had a small stomach, and they monitored it over the next few weeks because failure to grow would mean an earlier delivery. One baby (B) was eating a lot more than the other! Baby A's stomach started to grow slowly; this was a great relief.

I enjoyed being pregnant for the most part. It wasn't easy; nor was it glamorous, but it was a feeling I had been seeking. I was exactly where I wanted to be in my life. I was tired, hormonal and hungry all of the time, but making the decision to not be employed made the whole experience far easier. I was able to cope with everything that pregnancy had to throw at me, without the spectre of work performance, long commutes and regular daytime appointments weighing me down. Thankfully, Mike was very supportive of my decision, even though it was going to put more pressure on us financially. What also made my pregnancy special was that I was able to share it with my sister. We were both pregnant, four months apart, allowing us to spend time in the summer together.

Mike and I attended a one-day twins and multiples workshop. We signed up because I was interested in learning certain topics such as double breastfeeding, and I needed advice on my birthing plan. Mike wanted to know everything he could, as he hadn't had much experience caring for babies before. The day was very informative. It helped us prepare for the realities of parenting more than one baby, and we got to meet other couples in the same position that we were in. We learnt about what to expect during natural labour and caesarean births (a surgical procedure where they deliver babies through incisions in the abdomen and uterus). I was put off when the lady in the workshop explained that after the first baby is delivered, the second might turn and become breached (when a baby is born bottom first instead of headfirst). If this were to become the situation, then I would have two options:

1. The doctor could put his hand inside of my vagina to twist and pull the baby out
2. It would result in an emergency operation.

Neither options sounded great, so I decided the best choice was to have an elective caesarean section. This way, I would be able to discuss with the consultant which day I would like to give birth, and it would all be planned. The only hesitation I had to overcome was that there could be as many as twenty hospital staff present in the room during the course of the procedure. Clearly, it wouldn't be the somewhat intimate birthing I may have originally thought. It was the right choice for me, though.

I was now thirty-six weeks, two days, pregnant. Preterm birth is when a baby is born before thirty-seven completed weeks of pregnancy. For this particular hospital, full-term for twins was thirty-seven weeks. I had requested for the delivery to be on July 12th, but the hospital didn't perform C-sections on a Tuesday. I found out they had moved my delivery to Monday on the Thursday preceding my operation, when I was about to have more steroid injections.

If a baby was at risk of being born too early, giving the mother steroids before the birth could help her unborn baby's lungs to develop more quickly. This reduced the risk of serious complications or the newborn dying. Babies who were born very early could have trouble breathing because their lungs weren't yet fully developed. One 'course' of antenatal steroid treatment usually consisted of two injections given twenty-four hours apart. This gave many preterm babies a much better chance of survival. The shots were injected into the muscle of my buttocks. The nurse was laughing at me because I attended my appointment with a bag full of ice. I pulled my trousers down and bent over the bed, and after she iced the area, she injected me. This was the most painful injection out of them all; it was an intense stinging sensation that felt like it went on forever. After she finished, I was left sore and dreading my injection on Saturday. The second injection was just as intense as the first. I remembered cursing under my breath as she was administering it.

We entered the hospital at 7am on Monday, July 11th (thirty-six weeks, six days). I was nervous. Once seen, Mike and I were accompanied to the recovery room, and we were asked to change into a hospital gown. I wasn't allowed to wear jewellery or nail polish. I was relaxing, and I was texting a few people.

I asked the nurse, "Around what time could I expect to be seen?"

She replied, "It all depends on if there are any emergencies that come in. However, the doctor and medical team won't arrive until 8am."

After an hour and fifteen minutes, the nurse shouted, "OK, Michael, put your scrubs on. We are going now."

Michael questioned the nurse, "What now?"

At the time, I was messaging my sister. I was so mixed with emotions that I messaged her, "Aaaarrgghh, we have been called downstairs to have the babies!"

She replied, "Wow, that's quick, good luck, and let us know when you are finished."

"Hurry up, Mike; they are leaving," I shouted out to him as he was following behind, hopping, trying to put one of his surgical shoe covers on.

When we entered the clinically white room, I felt like I was on death row. The room was spacious, with a few metal trays surrounding the two beds in the middle. There was also a clock on the wall, which I couldn't stop staring at. It was 08:25. The nurse asked me to sit up on the bed with my feet flat on the floor, and she injected a local anaesthetic into my cannula, which was placed on my left hand. I was then asked to cuddle a pillow and not to move as they injected a spinal block into my back to numb the lower part of my body. This allowed me to be awake during the procedure. After a few minutes, they tested my legs by spraying cold water to check and see if I could feel anything. It was a strange sensation; I felt nothing. I was then lifted on to the other bed. Mike sat to the right of me, and to my left sat a nurse. I had a blue screen right in front of me so I couldn't see anything. I had prepared music on my iPhone to help me relax. Once the procedure started, every so often, I would be told that, "You will feel some pressure." It actually felt like I had an elephant sitting on my chest.

At one point, Mike stood up and peered over the screen. As he sat down, I asked him what he saw, and he said, "Your insides, and a lot of blood." I laughed. It was a strange new experience. To feel someone tugging on my tummy made me want to peer over the screen myself.

I was enjoying the whole experience, it felt unreal, and I was still half expecting to wake up from a dream. A few minutes later, at 09:13, I heard a little cry.

"Here is your son." The words seemed so surreal. The nurse handed him to Mike, and as he passed him over to me, he said, "He is amazing, and so tiny." Ethan (Baby A) weighed 5.5lbs.

I never heard the next cry, so I asked if everything was okay.

The nurse replied, "Yes, she is just having her checks."

Then Mike handed me over our daughter, laughing. "Our beautiful girl, she has a full head of hair."

Gabrielle (Baby B) was born at 09:15 and weighed 6.6lbs. She was the biggest out of the pair. They were born within two minutes of each other and were both healthy. I came downstairs pregnant and was returning to the ward as a mummy! I didn't know how to react or how to feel. I had waited my whole life for this moment, and now I didn't know what to do. Was I immediately supposed to be attached? We now had two babies fully reliant on us for the rest of our lives.

I maintained close skin-to-skin contact immediately after my delivery. Both Ethan and Gabrielle found a good attachment to my breasts, and I was lucky enough not to experience any issues. I found breastfeeding a natural way to create a loving bond; they took to it quickly. However, I decided to combination feed them (breast and bottle) so that Mike and our relatives could also help look after them. I wanted Mike to be involved as much as possible – and not just that, but if I needed a bit of sleep, he could take care of them without having to wake me.

The first few nights in the hospital were difficult; Mike was sleeping in the armchair, and I was struggling to move, having just had a major operation. On the same day I had them, I tried to get up from the bed and walk. I didn't just want to lie there, and I had heard that if you didn't walk around, it could take longer to be discharged from the hospital (although I didn't know if that had any truth in it.) Then I was moved from the recovery area up to a private room, which was compact. It was a struggle to fit both of us in the room, our bags, and two mobile baby beds, but we appreciated the privacy of the room, which we wouldn't have been given with just one baby. Mike was in and out of the sterilising room, cleaning bottles and updating the family. Neither of us were able to sleep during the night. Our instincts kept telling us to check the babies, to see if they were still breathing. But we didn't need to, since the babies' vitals and mine were being regularly monitored by nurses throughout the night.

After giving birth we were longing for some quiet time with our babies and also to try and get some much-needed rest. Unfortunately, being in a very frantic ward, with seemingly overwhelmed nursing staff, it made it feel impossible to rest and relax, with so many people rushing around. I would later find out that this was the start of a journey to sleeplessness, and that to this day, I am only just starting to get over it. However, it was all worth it.

We remained in the hospital for four days with no complications.

The next few months until the first year were extremely challenging. The days when I could just pop to the shops seemed so distant. We managed to get the twins into a routine with help from a maternity nurse, Jen. She helped us a lot from the birth of the twins, training them into a feeding and sleeping routine. She also taught me how to bathe them. In addition to this, Jen also helped develop my confidence with double breastfeeding and carrying them at the same time. There was a lot of information that I needed to digest straightaway, and I wasn't fully recovered from surgery.

I was embarrassed and shy to breastfeed in public, but I was fortunate to find a network of local mums that helped and supported me.

Everything from the start has been a learning process for all of us. The twins are growing up perfectly; both are very active and extremely inquisitive. Gabrielle learned to walk at eleven months and Ethan at thirteen months. Both have started to talk quite a bit. Gabrielle and Ethan excel in different skill sets and have different personalities. Gabrielle was quicker in learning to communicate, whereas Ethan was more advanced with his motor skills. He was a lot more independent and had slept in his own bed and room from six months on. Gabrielle, on the other hand, suffers from bad separation anxiety and night terrors; she still co-sleeps with us. At around nine months, we did have a sleep specialist come and help; she wanted us to try controlled crying. This involved waiting a set number of minutes while your baby is crying, without picking them up, to see if they drop off to sleep again. For us, this didn't work. Instead, it made Gabrielle act more withdrawn during the daytime. She wouldn't play; she just sat in the corner distancing herself from everyone, so at that point we decided to stop it. However, for a lot of other parents, this training method works. I have had comments such as "I'm making a rod for my own back" or "If you start that, she will never sleep alone." This might be correct but I am happy with this current situation, as it means we all get some sleep and, I know the day she leaves my room would be the day both my babies have grown up and no longer want to sleep with mummy so, I am in no rush to give that up.

I try to spend as much one to one time as I can with them on a daily basis; so, they can flourish as individuals, as well as twins. Nothing makes me feel prouder than watching them grow up and develop. The innocence in their smiles when they first experience or enjoy something is food for the soul! They change a little bit every day, and I am grateful that I haven't had to miss any of these moments.

We are very much in awe of them and loved them much more than they would ever know. We were so glad that all our suffering had finally ended. These precious rainbow babies were worth every fighting minute.

Just after they turned two years old, Mike and I enrolled the twins into nursery, and I started to think about going back to work. I had worked my whole life up to this point, and I found that being a stay at home mum for two years had seriously affected both my self-confidence and finances. Supporting a new family was more expensive than I ever imagined and of course, we had to buy two sets of most things. Our monthly shopping trips were in complete contrast to our previous existence as a couple. Six hundred nappies, a dozen boxes of formula, baby wipes, medicine, and creams, plus an endless supply of new clothes and toys to keep up with their rapid development. We were lucky that my sister passed down some clothes and toys that she had given her children. This helped us undoubtedly.

It was time to work again. I was fortunate that an opening was made available with my previous employer in the travel industry. I knew that I missed the camaraderie of the office and having an adult (non-baby related) conversation. On my first day back at work, I found myself feeling apprehensive whilst I was walking around the office and seeing all of the new faces. Our company had grown significantly and moved location, plus I was in a new role. Professionally speaking, at that moment, the world seemed to have left me behind. Fortunately, Vicky was very supportive; she had given birth to a little girl during my absence, and now, as a mum, she understood my situation. Vicky offered me a position in the company that had flexible hours; this allowed me to re-balance my life between working whilst being an active mother.

After three months of returning to work, the relationship between Vicky and myself had been better than ever. My confidence in the workplace finally returned back to where it was previously.

I have had time to contemplate my journey, and upon reflection, I can honestly say it has just been plain hard. Nothing could have prepared me for all the changes I would experience, from years of suffering from depression, to the trials and tribulations of the treatment. My body had changed beyond recognition throughout this process, and my overactive mind often thought about more than I could cope with.

However, I am thankful that I found the courage to persist with everything and I am eternally grateful for all the people that helped me along my journey. My heart is now full. I have my babies; I have my family and I am looking forward to what the future brings. Ethan and Gabrielle, thank you for being such brave warriors and for allowing me to become your mummy. Michael, thank you for never giving up and for giving me the strength and courage to keep going – your support has been inexhaustible.

REFERENCES

CRP CLINIC- DR HASSAN SHEHATA:
Website: https://www.miscarriageclinic.co.uk
Telephone: 01372 232221/0208 4019928
Email: office@crpclinic.co.uk

FERTILITY ASSIST-DR NATALY ATTALA:
Website: http://fertilityassist.co.uk
Telephone: 07445 710046
Email: info@fertilityassist.co.uk

MISCARRIAGE ASSOCIATION:
Website: www.miscarriageassociation.org.uk
Telephone: 01924 200799
Email: info@miscarriageassociation.org.uk